Property of the
Commonwealth of Pennsylvania
ESEA Title II 1972

P9-EMC-657

821.08   Hine, Al, ed
HIN
            From other   5668
            lands

DATE			
CONWAY			
FEB 2 4 1999			

5668

Blairsville Junior High School
Blairsville, Pennsylvania

@ THE BAKER & TAYLOR CO.

Blairsville Junior High School
Blairsville, Pennsylvania

FROM OTHER LANDS

❦ ❦ ❦

Also edited by Al Hine

THIS LAND IS MINE

FROM OTHER LANDS

Poetry That Makes History Live

EDITED BY
AL HINE

❦ ❦ ❦

J. B. LIPPINCOTT COMPANY

Philadelphia and New York

Copyright © 1969 by Al Hine
ALL RIGHTS RESERVED
Printed in the United States of America
Library of Congress Catalog Card Number: 72-82404
FIRST EDITION
Typography by Tere LoPrete

ACKNOWLEDGMENTS

For the right to reprint the copyrighted poems in this volume, the editor is indebted to the following poets, their families, agents, and publishers:

Jonathan Cape Ltd. for "Headline History" from COLLECTED POEMS by William Plomer.
Chatto and Windus Ltd. and the Author's Literary Estate for "Break of Day at the Trenches" from COLLECTED POEMS by Isaac Rosenberg.
The Christian Science Monitor and Norma Farber for "The Night Before America" by Norma Farber, © 1956 The Christian Science Publishing Society, all rights reserved.
William Collins Sons & Co., Ltd. for "The Fall of Llywelyn" by Beddyn Farr, translated by D. M. Lloyd, from A BOOK OF WALES.
Dodd, Mead & Co., Inc. for "Lepanto" from THE COLLECTED POEMS OF G. K. CHESTERTON, copyright 1932 by Dodd, Mead & Co., Inc. Copyright renewed 1959 by Oliver Chesterton.
Doubleday & Company, Inc. and Mrs. George Bambridge for "St. Helena Lullaby," copyright 1910 by Rudyard Kipling; "Romulus & Remus," copyright 1908 by Rudyard Kipling; "Reeds of Runnymede," copyright 1911 by Rudyard Kipling; "A Pict Song," "The Widow at Windsor," and "Song to Mithras." All from RUDYARD KIPLING'S VERSE: DEFINITIVE EDITION.
Faber and Faber Limited for "Brother Fire" by Louis MacNeice from COLLECTED POEMS and "The Ballad of the Goodly Fere" from PERSONAE by Ezra Pound.
Ronald E. Gurney and Messrs. Sidgewick and Jackson Ltd. for "Ypres" by Ivor Gurney.
The Hogarth Press Ltd. and Mrs. Elna Lucas for "Proud Motherhood" from POEMS FOR SPAIN by F. L. Lucas.
New Directions Publishing Corporation for "Ballad of the Goodly Fere" from PERSONAE by Ezra Pound. Copyright 1926 by Ezra Pound.
New Statesman for "War Poem" by Richard West from *New Statesman:* 14 October, 1966.
Harold Ober Associates, Inc. for "When Hannibal Crossed the Alps" from THE CHILDREN'S BELLS by Eleanor Farjeon, published by Henry Z. Walck, Inc. copyright © 1960 by Eleanor Farjeon.
Oxford University Press for "Brother Fire" from THE COLLECTED POEMS OF LOUIS MACNEICE, edited by E. R. Dodds. Copyright © The Estate of Louis MacNeice, 1966.
Random House, Inc. Alfred A. Knopf, Inc. for "The Old Ships" and "War Song of the Saracens" from COLLECTED POEMS by James Elroy Flecker, published by Alfred A. Knopf, Inc.
Schocken Books Inc. for "Break of Day in the Trenches" from COLLECTED POEMS by Isaac Rosenberg, copyright © 1949 by Schocken Books Inc.
Scorpion Press for "Annotations of Auschwitz" from ONCE BITTEN TWICE BITTEN by Peter Porter.
Charles Scribner's Sons for "Zola" from THE CHILDREN OF THE NIGHT by Edwin Arlington Robinson. (1897)
A. P. Watt & Son for "Drake's Drum" from POEMS NEW AND OLD by Sir Henry Newbolt, published by John Murray Ltd., London; "Lepanto" from COLLECTED POEMS OF G. K. CHESTERTON; "A Pict Song," "Reeds of Runnymede," and "Romulus and Remus" from THE DEFINITIVE EDITION OF RUDYARD KIPLING'S VERSE, "The Widow at Windsor" from BARRACK ROOM BALLADS by Rudyard Kipling, "Song to Mithras" from PUCK OF POOK'S HILL by Rudyard Kipling, and "A St. Helena Lullaby" from REWARDS AND FAIRIES by Rudyard Kipling.

CONTENTS

❦ ❦ ❦

(5)

INTRODUCTION

❧ ❧ ❧

History begins in verse.

The first poets celebrated their own feats, exploits of their friends and the glories of their tribes. Primitive rhythms, linked with rhyme or alliteration, made important events easier to remember, and (one may assume) fancied them up in the telling to reflect merit on special hero, tribe, or nation. The same rules hold true today although, unhappily, too many of our best poets turn their backs on current history. But, on the traditional level, you have only to listen to a chauvinistic American popular tune like *The Ballad of the Green Berets* and consider that, in North Viet Nam, patriotic peasants are singing their own ballads, quite as simpleminded, just as rousing, equally one-sided.

This one-sidedness is important to remember in reading the verse collected here. Almost always the enemy is a deep-dyed villain and "our side," depending on who is writing the poem, is clean-limbed, brave, and idealistic. Very rarely, although the more so as verse approaches modern times, is there any attempt at fair-mindedness. There has never been a despot so cruel and nasty that there wasn't someone around to write heroic verse in his praise. There have been few heroes who didn't have mud slung at them in rhyme and meter. With this in mind, a certain balance may be preserved in reading what follows.

(13)

My standards of selection have been simple and subjective. I have included only verses that pleased me or that, for reasons of time-resisting fame or importance of subject, have overborne my own dislike. The severest handicap has been the English language itself. Keeping to English verse, one is held close, if not to British and American history, at least to such events in other histories as have appealed to English and American poets. There is a whole wealth of European history—and verse—only touched on here because good translations are lacking. There is an even greater wealth (and a much more disgraceful omission) in the history—and verse—of Africa and Asia. Most English verse is white man's verse and, with a complacency that looks shocking in 1968, views more than half the world simply as a platter offering helpings of commerce and land and cheap labor to Europe.

Notes have been supplied to aid, but not to insult the reader's intelligence and the date given before each poem is to identify as closely as possible the year when the event took place. In general, I have not changed or modernized most texts, although occasionally I have shifted English spellings in modern verse to the American usage—*honor,* instead of *honour,* and the like. Cuts in individual poems have been indicated where they occur or in notes.

As I said in the introduction to *This Land Is Mine* (American History in Verse): The only use of this or any other anthology is to open doors. I would add: doors not only to verse, but to the past that belongs to every one of us.

Rome——November, 1968

THE OLD SHIPS

by James Elroy Flecker

I have seen old ships sail like swans asleep
Beyond the village that men still call Tyre,
With leaden age o'er cargoed, dipping deep
For Famagusta and the hidden sun
That rings black Cyprus with a lake of fire;
And all those ships were certainly so old
Who knows how oft with squat and noisy gun,
Questing brown slaves or Syrian oranges,
The pirate Genoese
Hell-raked them till they rolled
Blood, water, fruit, and corpses in the hold.
But now through friendly seas they softly run,
Painted the mid-sea blue or shore-sea green,
Still patterned with the vine and grapes in gold.
But I have seen,
Pointing her shapely shadows from the dawn
And image tumbled on a rose-swept bay,
A drowsy ship of some yet older day;
And, wonder's breath indrawn,
Thought I—who knows—who knows—but in that same
(Fished up beyond Aeae, patched up new
—Stern painted brighter blue—)
That talkative, bald-headed seaman came
(Twelve patient comrades sweating at the oar)
From Troy's doom-crimson shore,
And with great lies about his wooden horse
Set the crew laughing, and forgot his course.
It was so old a ship—who knows—who knows?
—And yet so beautiful, I watched in vain

To see the mast burst open with a rose,
And the whole deck put on its leaves again.

❦

The talkative, bald-headed seaman is Ulysses. Nobody knows the precise date of the siege of Troy, but there was a Troy or Ilium and, in song and story, in a half-blend of history and legend, it has furnished a focus for much of European history since. Rome's proudest claim was to trace its foundation to Aeneas, the most notable Trojan escapee, and medieval English (and other European) monarchs sought legitimacy in carefully worked out charts of descent from Greek or Trojan heroes.

1150 B.C.

JEPTHAH'S DAUGHTER

by Alfred, Lord Tennyson

The daughter of the warrior Gileadite,
　A maiden pure; as when she went along
From Mizpeh's tower'd gate with welcome light,
　With timbrel and with song.

My words leap forth: "Heaven heads the count of crimes
　With that wild oath." She rendered answer high:
"Not so; nor once alone, a thousand times
　I would be born and die.

"Single I grew, like some green plant, whose root
　Creeps to the garden water-pipes beneath,
Feeding the flower; but ere my flower to fruit
　Changed, I was ripe for death.

"My God, my land, my father—these did move
　Me from my bliss of life, that Nature gave,
Lower'd softly with a threefold cord of love
　Down to a silent grave.

"And I went mourning, 'No fair Hebrew boy
　Shall smile away my maiden blame among
The Hebrew mothers'—emptied of all joy,
　Leaving the dance and song,

"Leaving the olive-gardens far below,
　Leaving the promise of my bridal bower,

The valleys of grape-loaded vines that grow
　　Beneath the battled tower.

"The light white cloud swam over us. Anon
　　We heard the lion roaring from his den;
We saw the large white stars rise one by one,
　　Or, from the darken'd glen,

"Saw God divide the night with flying flame,
　　And thunder on the everlasting hills.
I heard Him, for He spake, and grief became
　　A solemn scorn of ills.

"When the next day was rolled into the sky,
　　Strength came to me that equall'd my desire.
How beautiful a thing it was to die
　　For God and for my sire!

"It comforts me in this one thought to dwell,
　　That I subdued me to my father's will;
Because the kiss he gave me, ere I fell,
　　Sweetens the spirit still.

"Moreover it is written that my race
　　Hew'd Ammon, hip and thigh, from Aroer
On Arnon unto Minneth." Here her face
　　Glow'd as I looked at her.

She lock'd her lips: she left me where I stood:
　　"Glory to God," she sang, and past afar,
Thridding the sombre boskage of the wood,
　　Toward the morning star.

Jepthah the Gileadite, commander of the Israeli army, made a rash vow before battle with the Ammonites: If he won the battle he would make a sacrifice of the first person he met on returning home. He won the battle, but the first person to greet him at home was his virgin daughter. It was she who insisted that she be killed, after a two-month respite in the mountains, to fulfill her father's promise. The next to last verse of the final stanza must stand out as one of the wildest absurdities in all Victorian verse, close to Jabberwocky.

1100 B.C.

From SAMSON AGONISTES

by John Milton

Occasions drew me early to this city,
And as the gates I enter'd with Sun-rise,
The morning Trumpets Festival proclaim'd
Through each high street: little I had dispatch't,
When all abroad was rumor'd that this day
Samson should be brought forth, to shew the people
Proof of his might strength in feats and games;
I sorrow'd at his captive state, but minded
Not to be absent at that spectacle.
The building was a spacious Theatre,
Half round, on two main Pillars vaulted high,
With seats where all the Lords and each degree
Of sort, might sit in order to behold,
The other side was op'n, where the throng
On banks and scaffolds, under Skie might stand;
I, among these, aloof obscurely stood.
The Feast and noon grew high, and Sacrifice
Had fill'd their hearts with mirth, high chear, and wine,
When to their sports they turn'd. Immediately
Was Samson as a public servant brought
In their state Livery clad: before him Pipes
And timbrels, on each side went armed guards,
Both horse and foot before him and behind,
Archers and Slingers, Cataphracts and Spears.
At sight of him the people with a shout
Rifted the Air, clamoring their god with praise,
Who had made their dreadful enemy their thrall.
He patient but undaunted where they led him,
Came to the place, and what was set before him

Which without help of eye, might be assay'd,
To heave, pull, draw, or break, he still perform'd
All with incredible, stupendious force,
None daring to appear Antagonist.
At length, for intermission sake they led him
Between the pillars; he his guide requested
(For so from such as nearer stood we heard)
As over-tir'd to let him lean a while
With both his arms, on those two massie Pillars,
That to the arched roof gave main support.
He unsuspicious led him; which when Samson
Felt in his arms, with head a while inclin'd,
And eyes fast fixt he stood, as one who pray'd,
Or some great matter in his mind revolv'd.
At last with head erect thus cried aloud:
"Hitherto, Lords, what your commands impos'd
I have perform'd, as reason was, obeying,
Not without wonder or delight beheld.
Now, of my own accord such other trial
I mean to shew you of my strength, yet greater;
As with amaze shall strike all who behold."
This utter'd, straining all his nerves, he bow'd:
As with the force of winds and waters pent,
When Mountains tremble, those two massie Pillars
With horrible convulsion to and fro,
He tugg'd, he shook, till down thy came and drew
The whole roof after them with burst of thunder
Upon the heads of all who sat beneath,
Lords, Ladies, Captains, Counsellors, or Priests,
Their choice nobility and flower, not only
Of this but each Philistian City round,
Met from all parts to solemnize this Feast.
Samson with these inmixt, inevitably
Pull'd down the same destruction on himself.

Samson of Dan, legendary—historic Israelite strong man, was captured and blinded by his Philistine enemies, but, at a public exhibition, pulled down the heathen temple on his captors and on himself. Milton, in good Puritan tradition, is careful to let his Samson bring the worst destruction upon "lords, ladies . . . choice nobility," and spare the common spectators.

950 B.C.

SAUL

by Robert Browning

Said Abner, "At last thou art come! Ere I tell, ere thou speak,
Kiss my cheek, wish me well!" Then I wished it, and did kiss
  his cheek.
And he, "Since the king, O my friend, for thy countenance sent,
Neither drunken nor eaten have we; nor until from his tent
Thou return with the joyful assurance the king liveth yet,
Shall our lips with the honey be bright, with the water be wet.
For out of the black mid-tent's silence, a space of three days,
Not a sound has escaped to thy servants, of prayer nor of praise,
To betoken that Saul and the Spirit have ended their strife,
And that, faint in his triumph, the monarch sinks back upon
  life."

                              Then I, as was meet,
Knelt down to the God of my fathers, and rose on my feet,
And ran o'er the sand burnt to powder. The tent was unlooped;
I pulled up the spear that obstructed, and under I stooped;
Hands and knees on the slippery grass patch, all withered and
  gone,
That extends to the second enclosure, I groped my way on
Till I felt where the foldskirts fly open. Then once more I prayed,
And opened the foldskirts and entered, and was not afraid
But spoke, "Here is David, thy servant!" And no voice replied.
At the first I saw naught but the blackness: but soon I descried
A something more black than the blackness—the vast, the upright
Main prop which sustains the pavilion: and slow into sight
Grew a figure against it, gigantic and blackest of all.
Then a sunbeam that burst through the tent-roof, showed Saul.

(23)

He stood as erect as that tent prop, both arms stretched out wide
On the great cross-support in the center, that goes to each side;
He relaxed not a muscle, but hung there,—as, caught in his pangs
And waiting his change, the king-serpent all heavily hangs,
Far away from his kind, in the pine, till deliverance come
With the springtime—so agonized Saul, drear and stark, blind
and dumb.

Ay, to save and redeem and restore him, maintain at the height
This perfection,—succeeded with life's dayspring, death's minute
of night?
Interpose at the difficult minute, snatch Saul, the mistake,
Saul, the failure, the ruin he seems now,—and bid him awake
From the dream, the probation, the prelude, to find himself set
Clear and safe in new light and new life,—a new harmony yet
To be run, and continued, and ended—who knows?—or endure!
The man taught enough by life's dream, of the rest to make sure.
By the pain-throb, triumphantly winning intensified bliss,
And the next world's reward and repose, by the struggle in this.

❦

Saul served as half-king of a confederation of desert tribes, his royal
power complete as a military commander, but circumscribed in non-
military affairs by the power of the "prophets"—part holy men, part
civic arbiters, David, whose kingship was to outshine even Saul's, was
at the time of the poem an ambiguous figure, a royal protégé, harp-
player, fledgling warrior, and the only person in all Israel who could
bring the king out of those dark, melancholic moods into which he
sometimes plunged.

753 B.C.

ROMULUS AND REMUS

by Rudyard Kipling

Oh, little did the Wolf-Child care—
  When first he planned his home,
What City should arise and bear
  The weight and state of Rome.

A shiftless, westward-wandering tramp,
  Checked by the Tiber flood,
He reared a wall around his camp
  Of uninspired mud.

But when his brother leaped the Wall
  And mocked its height and make,
He guessed the failure of it all
  And slew him for its sake.

Swift was the blow—swift as the thought
  Which showed him in that hour
How unbelief may bring to naught
  The early steps of Power.

Forseeing Time's imperilled hopes
  Of Glory, Grace, and Love—
All singers, Caesars, artists, Popes—
  Would fail as Remus throve,

He sent his brother to the Gods,
  And, when the fit was o'er,
Went on collecting turves and clods
  To build the Wall once more!

(25)

In classical tradition, the twin brothers, Romulus and Remus, were reared by a motherly she-wolf. They grew to manhood and to tribal leadership together. But Romulus proudly built a wall around his settlement and Remus scornfully jumped over it to show how petty he found his brother's pretensions. It was then, as Kipling chronicles, that Romulus killed Remus and, full of an angry vision of greatness, set about building Rome in earnest and, naturally, in more than a day.

701 B.C.

SENNACHERIB

by George Gordon, Lord Byron

The Assyrian came down like a wolf on the fold,
And his cohorts were gleaming in purple and gold;
And the sheen of their spears was like stars on the sea,
When the blue wave rolls nightly on deep Galilee.

Like the leaves of the forest when summer is green,
That host with their banners at sunset were seen;
Like the leaves of the forest when autumn hath blown,
That host on the morrow lay withered and strown.

For the Angel of Death spread his wings on the blast,
And breathed in the face of the foe as he pass'd;
And the eyes of the sleepers wax'd deadly and chill,
And their hearts but once heaved, and forever grew still!

And there lay the steed with his nostril all wide;
But through it there roll'd not the breath of his pride:
And the foam of his gasping lay white on the turf,
And cold as the spray of the rock-beating surf.

And there lay the rider distorted and pale,
With the dew on his brow, and the rust on his mail;
And the tents were all silent, the banners alone,
The lances uplifted, the trumpet unblown.

And the widows of Ashur are loud in their wail,
And the idols are broke in the temple of Baal;
And the might of the Gentile, unsmote by the sword,
Hath melted like snow in the glance of the Lord!

(27)

Sennacherib of Assyria did move his army against Israel, but modern historians don't accept the biblical version of the outcome as cheerfully as Byron. Actually, the Assyrians took almost all major cities except Jerusalem and the kingdom of Judah paid tribute for many years after.

SARDANAPALUS

by Henry Howard, Earl of Surrey

The Assyrian king—in peace, with foul desire
And filthy lusts that stained his regal heart—
In war, that should set princely hearts on fire,
Did yield vanquisht for want of martial art.
The dint of swords from kisses seemèd strange;
And harder than his lady's side, his targe;
From glutton feasts to soldier's fare, a change;
His helmet, far above a garland's charge.
Who scarce the name of manhood did retain,
Drenchèd in sloth and womanish delight.
Feeble in sprite, unpatient of pain,
When he had lost his honor and his right
(Proud, time of wealth: in storms, appall'd with dread)
Murder'd himself, to show some manful deed.

❧

Sardanapalus was a romanized spelling for Assurbanipal, the last king of Assyria, as totally ineffective as his fierce predecessors (like Sennacherib) had been energetic. His name, in semi-classical legend, became a synonym for decadent effeminacy and his suicide a highly normal end to a career of wicked luxury. Howard, at least, allows him lady loves without lessening his disapproval.

THE VISION OF BELSHAZZAR

by George Gordon, Lord Byron

The King was on his throne,
The Satraps throng'd the hall;
A thousand bright lamps shone
O'er that high festival.
A thousand cups of gold,
In Judah deem'd divine—
Jehovah's vessels hold
The godless Heathen's wine.

In that same hour and hall,
The fingers of a hand
Came forth against the wall,
And wrote as if on sand:
The fingers of a man;—
A solitary hand
Along the letters ran,
And traced them like a wand.

The monarch saw, and shook,
And bade no more rejoice;
All bloodless wax'd his look,
And tremulous his voice.
"Let the men of lore appear,
The wisest of the earth,
And expound the words of fear,
Which mar our royal mirth."

Chaldea's seers are good,
But here they had no skill;

And the unknown letters stood
Untold and awful still.
And Babel's men of age
Are wise and deep in lore;
But now they were not sage,
They saw—but knew no more.

A captive in the land,
A stranger and a youth,
He heard the king's command,
He saw that writing's truth.
The lamps around were bright,
The prophecy in view;
He read it on that night,—
The morrow proved it true.

"Balshazzar's grave is made,
His kingdom pass'd away,
He, in the balance weigh'd,
Is light and worthless clay,
The shroud, his robe of state,
His canopy the stone;
The Mede is at his gate!
The Persian on his throne!"

Belshazzar was grandson of the great Nebuchadnezzar who spread the rule of his Babylonian Empire through Syria and Palestine and as far as Tyre. The vision at the monarch's feast was accurately interpreted by Daniel, a captive Jew, as foretelling the conquest of Babylon by Cyrus the Great of Persia.

508 B.C.

HORATIUS AT THE BRIDGE

by Thomas Babington Macaulay

Lars Porsena of Clusium,
  By the Nine Gods he swore
That the great house of Tarquin
  Should suffer wrong no more.
By the Nine Gods he swore it,
  And named a trysting-day,
And bade his messengers ride forth,
East and west and south and north,
  To summon his array.

East and west and south and north
  The messengers ride fast,
And tower and town and cottage
  Have heard the trumpet's blast.
Shame on the false Etruscan
  Who lingers in his home,
When Porsena of Clusium
  Is on the march to Rome.

There be thirty chosen prophets,
  The wisest of the land,
Who always by Lars Porsena
  Both morn and evening stand.
Evening and morn the thirty
  Have turned the verses o'er,
Traced from the right on linen white
  By mighty seers of yore.

And with one voice the thirty
  Have their glad answer given:
"Go forth, go forth, Lars Porsena,—
  Go forth, beloved of heaven!
Go, and return in glory
  To Clusium's royal dome,
And hang round Nurscia's altars
  The golden shields of Rome!"

And now hath every city
  Sent up her tale of men;
The foot are fourscore thousand,
  The horse are thousands ten.
Before the gates of Sutrium
  Is met the great array;
A proud man was Lars Porsena
  Upon the trysting-day.

Now from the rock Tarpeian,
  Could the wan burghers spy
The line of blazing villages
  Red in the midnight sky.
The fathers of the city,
  They sat all night and day,
For every hour some horseman came
  With tidings of dismay.

I wis, in all the Senate
  There was no heart so bold
But sore it ached, and fast it beat,
  When that ill news was told.
Forthwith up rose the Consul,
  Up rose the Fathers all;
In haste they girded up their gowns,
  And hied them to the wall.

(33)

They held a council, standing
    Before the River-Gate:
Short time was there, ye well may guess,
    For musing or debate.
Out spake the Consul roundly:
    "The bridge must straight go down;
For, since Janiculum is lost,
    Naught else can save the town."

Just then a scout came flying,
    All wild with haste and fear:
"To arms! to arms! Sir Consul,—
    Lars Porsena is here."
On the low hills to westward
    The Consul fixed his eye,
And saw the swarthy storm of dust
    Rise fast along the sky.

But the Consul's brow was sad,
    And the Consul's speech was low,
And darkly looked he at the wall,
    And darkly at the foe:
"Their van will be upon us
    Before the bridge goes down;
And if they once may win the bridge,
    What hope to save the town?"

Then outspake brave Horatius,
    The Captain of the Gate:
"To every man upon this earth
    Death cometh soon or late.
And how can man die better
    Than facing fearful odds
For the ashes of his fathers
    And the temples of his Gods?

"And for the tender mother
  Who dandled him to rest,
And for the wife who nurses
  His baby at her breast,
And for the holy maidens
  Who feed the eternal flame,—
To save them from false Sextus
  That wrought the deed of shame?

"Hew down the bridge, Sir Consul,
  With all the speed ye may;
I, with two more to help me,
  Will hold the foe in play.
In yon straight path a thousand
  May well be stopped by three:
Now who will stand on either hand,
  And keep the bridge with me?"

Then out spake Spurius Lartius,—
  A Ramnian bold was he:
"Lo, I will stand at thy right hand,
  And keep the bridge with thee."
Then out spake strong Herminius,—
  Of Titian blood was he:
"I will abide on thy left side,
  And keep the bridge with thee."

The Three stood calm and silent,
  And looked upon the foes,
And a great shout of laughter
  From all the vanguard rose;
And forth three chiefs came spurring
  Before that deep array;
To earth they sprang, their swords they drew,

And lifted high their shields and flew
   To win the narrow way.

Aunus, from green Tifernum,
   Lord of the Hill of Vines;
And Seius, whose eight hundred slaves
   Sicken in Ilva's mines;
And Picus, long to Clusium
   Vassal in peace and war,
Who led to fight his Umbrian powers
From that gray crag where, girt with towers,
The fortress of Nequinum lowers
   O'er the pale waves of Nar.

Stout Lartius hurled down Aunus
   Into the stream beneath;
Herminius struck at Seius;
   And clove him to the teeth;
At Picus brave Horatius
   Darted one fiery thrust,
And the proud Umbrian's gilded arms
   Clashed in the bloody dust.

But now no sound of laughter
   Was heard among the foes;
A wild and wrathful clamor
   From all the vanguard rose.
Six spears' lengths from the entrance,
   Halted that deep array,
And for a space no man came forth
   To win the narrow way.

But, hark! the cry is Astur:
   And lo! the ranks divide;

And the great lord of Luna
  Comes with his stately stride.
Upon his ample shoulders
  Clangs loud the fourfold shield,
And in his hand he shakes the brand
  Which none but he can wield.

He smiled on those bold Romans,
  A smile serene and high;
He eyed the flinching Tuscans,
  And scorn was in his eye.
Quoth he, "The she-wolf's litter
  Stand savagely at bay;
But will ye dare to follow,
  If Astur clears the way?"

Then, whirling up his broadsword
  With both hands to the height,
He rushed against Horatius,
  And smote with all his might.
With shield and blade Horatius
  Right deftly turned the blow.
The blow, though turned, came yet too nigh;
It missed his helm, but gashed his thigh.
The Tuscans raised a joyful cry
  To see the red blood flow.

He reeled, and on Herminius
  He leaned one breathing-space,
Then, like a wild-cat mad with wounds,
  Sprang right at Astur's face.
Through teeth and skull and helmet
  So fierce a thrust he sped,
The good sword stood a handbreadth out
  Behind the Tuscan's head.

(37)

And the great lord of Luna
  Fell at that deadly stroke,
As falls on Mount Avernus
  A thunder-smitten oak.
Far o'er the crashing forest
The giant arms he spread;
And the pale augurs, muttering low,
  Gaze on the blasted head.

On Astur's throat Horatius
  Right firmly pressed his heel,
And thrice and four times tugged amain,
  Ere he wrenched out the steel.
"And see," he cried, "the welcome,
  Fair guests, that waits you here!
What noble Lucumo comes next
  To taste our Roman cheer?"

But at his haughty challenge
  A sullen murmur ran,
Mingled with wrath and shame and dread,
  Along that glittering van.
There lacked not men of prowess,
  Nor men of lordly race,
For all Etruria's noblest
  Were round the fatal place.

Was none who would be foremost
  To lead such dire attack;
But those behind cried "Forward!"
  And those before cried "Back!"
And backward now, and forward,
  Wavers the deep array;
And on the tossing sea of steel
To and fro the standards reel,

And the victorious trumpet-peal
　　Dies fitfully away.

Yet one man for a moment
　　Strode out before the crowd;
Well known was he to all the three,
　　And they gave him greeting loud:
"Now welcome, welcome, Sextus!
　　Now welcome to thy home!
Why dost thou stay, and turn away?
　　Here lies the road to Rome."

Thrice looked he at the city;
　　Thrice looked he at the dead;
And thrice came on in fury,
　　And thrice turned back in dread;
And, white with fear and hatred,
　　Scowled at the narrow way
Where, wallowing in a pool of blood,
　　The bravest Tuscans lay.

But meanwhile axe and lever
　　Have manfully been plied;
And now the bridge hangs tottering
　　Above the boiling tide.
"Come back, come back, Horatius!"
　　Loud cried the Fathers all.—
"Back, Lartius! back, Herminius!
　　Back, ere the ruin fall!"

Back darted Spurius Lartius;—
　　Herminius darted back;
And, as they passed, beneath their feet
　　They felt the timbers crack.

(39)

But when they turned their faces,
   And on the farther shore
Saw brave Horatius stand alone,
   They would have crossed once more;

But with a crash like thunder
   Fell every loosened beam,
And, like a dam, the mighty wreck
   Lay right athwart the stream:
And a long shout of triumph
   Rose from the walls of Rome,
As to the highest turret-tops
   Was splashed the yellow foam.

Alone stood brave Horatius,
   But constant still in mind,—
Thrice thirty thousand foes before,
   And the broad flood behind.
"Down with him!" cried false Sextus,
   With a smile on his pale face;
"Now yield thee," cried Lars Porsena,
   "Now yield thee to our grace."

Round turned he, as not deigning
   Those craven ranks to see;
Naught spake he to Lars Porsena,
   To Sextus naught spake he;
But he saw on Palatinus
   The white porch of his home;
And he spake to the noble river
   That rolls by the towers of Rome:

"O Tiber! Father Tiber!
   To whom the Romans pray,

A Roman's life, a Roman's arms,
   Take thou in charge this day!"
So he spake, and, speaking, sheathed
   The good sword by his side,
And, with his harness on his back,
   Plunged headlong in the tide.

No sound of joy or sorrow
   Was heard from either bank,
But friends and foes in dumb surprise,
With parted lips and straining eyes,
   Stood gazing where he sank;
And when above the surges
   They saw his crest appear,
All Rome sent forth a rapturous cry,
And even the ranks of Tuscany
   Could scarce forbear to cheer.

But fiercely ran the current,
   Swollen high by months of rain,
And fast his blood was flowing;
   And he was sore in pain,
And heavy was his armor,
   And spent with changing blows;
And oft they thought him sinking,
   But still again he rose.

Never, I ween, did swimmer,
   In such an evil case,
Struggle through such a raging flood
   Safe to the landing-place;
But his limbs were borne up bravely
   By the brave heart within,
And our good Father Tiber
   Bare bravely up his chin.

(41)

"Curse on him!" quoth false Sextus,—
    "Will not the villain drown?
But for this stay, ere close of day
    We should have sacked the town!"
"Heaven help him!" quoth Lars Porsena,
    "And bring him safe to shore;
For such a gallant feat of arms
    Was never seen before."

And now he feels the bottom;
    Now on dry earth he stands;
Now round him throng the fathers
    To press his gory hands;
And now, with shouts and clapping,
    And noise of weeping loud,
He enters through the River-Gate,
    Borne by the joyous crowd.

They gave him of the corn-land,
    That was of public right,
As much as two strong oxen
    Could plough from morn till night;
And they made a molten image,
    And set it up on high,
And there it stands until this day
    To witness if I lie.

It stands in the Comitium,
    Plain for all folks to see,—
Horatius in his harness,
    Halting upon one knee;
And underneath is written,
    In letters all of gold,
How valiantly he kept the bridge
    In the brave days of old.

And still his name sounds stirring
    Unto the men of Rome,
As the trumpet-blast that cries to them
    To charge the Volscian home;
And wives still pray to Juno
    For boys with hearts as bold
As his who kept the bridge so well
    In the brave days of old.

And in the nights of winter,
    When the cold north-winds blow,
And the long howling of the wolves
    Is heard amidst the snow;
When round the lonely cottage
    Roars loud the tempest's din,
And the good logs of Algidus
    Roar louder yet within;

When the oldest cask is opened,
    And the largest lamp is lit;
When the chestnuts glow in the embers,
    And the kid turns on the spit;
When young and old in circle
    Around the firebrands close;
When the girls are weaving baskets,
    And the lads are shaping bows;

When the goodman mends his armor,
    And trims his helmet's plume;
When the goodwife's shuttle merrily
    Goes flashing through the loom;
With weeping and with laughter
    Still is the story told,
How well Horatius kept the bridge
    In the brave days of old.

I confess without apology to having trimmed as many verses as possible from Horatius without confusing the story. It's still the longest poem in this collection, but, as a rousing heroic narrative, holds its place at the top of its class. Nobody knows for certain whether there was or was not a real Horatius. There was an Etruscan attack by Lars Porsena in 1508, but authorities believe it succeeded temporarily until the Romans, under an early dictator Aulus Postumius, broke the Etruscan power for good at the Battle of Lake Regillus. Macaulay has another poem on this battle, but it can't match the ring and swing of Horatius.

False Sextus, a perfect old-time movie villain was a Roman who had deserted to the standards of Lars Porsena.

218 B.C.

WHEN HANNIBAL CROSSED THE ALPS

by Eleanor Farjeon

Hannibal crossed the Alps!
Hannibal crossed the Alps!
  With his black men,
  His brown men,
    His countrymen,
    His town-men,
  With his Gauls, and his Spaniards, his horses and elephants
Hannibal crossed the Alps!

Hannibal crossed the Alps!
Hannibal crossed the Alps!
    For his bowmen,
    His spearmen,
    His front men,
    His rear men,
His Gauls and his Spaniards, his horses and elephants,
Wanted the Roman scalps!
And *that's* why Hannibal, Hannibal, Hannibal,
Hannibal crossed the Alps!

Carthage, across the sea in North Africa, near where Tunis now stands, was Rome's only major rival, and Hannibal was its most notable general. He brought his army up through Spain and across Southern France to attack Rome from the hitherto impregnably protective Alps. Elephants and all, his horde swarmed almost within striking distance of Rome itself. But Hannibal was too far from his home base and lacked decent communications and support. The Romans turned back the threat, then followed Hannibal into Africa where the Carthaginian army was annihilated at the Battle of Zampa in 202 B.C. And Rome was left supreme for centuries.

54 B.C.

A PICT SONG

by Rudyard Kipling

Rome never looks where she treads.
  Always her heavy hooves fall
On our stomachs, our hearts or our heads;
  And Rome never heeds when we bawl.
Her sentries pass on—that is all,
  And we gather behind them in hordes,
And plot to reconquer the Wall,
  With only our tongues for our swords.

We are the Little Folk—we!
  Too little to love or to hate.
Leave us alone and you'll see
  How we can drag down the State!
We are the worm in the wood!
  We are the rot at the root!
We are the taint in the blood!
  We are the thorn in the foot!

Mistletoe killing an oak—
  Rats gnawing cables in two—
Moths making holes in a cloak—
  How they must love what they do!
Yes—and we Little Folk too,
  We are busy as they—
Working our works out of view—
  Watch, and you'll see it some day!

No indeed! We are not strong,
  But we know People that are.

Yes, and we'll guide them along
   To smash and destroy you in War.
We shall be slaves just the same?
   Yes, we have always been slaves,
But you—you will die of the shame,
   And then we shall dance on your graves!

We are the Little Folk, we, etc.

✿

Britain was important as a source of tin. Rome needed safe access to the mines, so Julius Caesar, not yet a monarch, but already a successful general, moved on the primitive island and established Roman control, but only, as Kipling points out, on the surface.

From *JULIUS CAESAR*

by *William Shakespeare*

ANTONY:
Friends, Romans, countrymen, lend me your ears;
I come to bury Caesar, not to praise him.
The evil that men do lives after them;
The good is oft interred with their bones;
So let it be with Caesar. The noble Brutus,
Hath told you Caesar was ambitious:
If it were so, it was a grievous fault,
And grievously hath Caesar answer'd it.
Here, under leave of Brutus and the rest—
For Brutus is an honorable man;
So are they all, all honorable men—
Come I to speak in Caesar's funeral.
He was my friend, faithful and just to me;
But Brutus says he was ambitious;
And Brutus is an honorable man.
He hath brought many captives home to Rome,
Whose ransoms did the general coffers fill:
Did this in Caesar seem ambitious?
When that the poor have cried, Caesar hath wept:
Ambition should be made of sterner stuff:
Yet Brutus says he was ambitious;
And Brutus is an honorable man.
You all did see that on the Lupercal
I thrice presented him a kingly crown,
Which he did thrice refuse: was this ambition?
Yet Brutus says he was ambitious;
And, sure, he is an honorable man.
I speak not to disprove what Brutus spoke,

But here I am to speak what I do know.
You all did love him once, not without cause:
What cause withholds you then to mourn for him?
O judgement! thou art fled to brutish beasts,
And men have lost their reason. Bear with me;
My heart is in the coffin there with Caesar,
And I must pause till it come back to me . . .

But yesterday, the word of Caesar might
Have stood against the world; now lies he there,
And none so poor to do him reverence.
O masters, if I were disposed to stir
Your hearts and minds to mutiny and rage,
I should do Brutus wrong, and Cassius wrong,
Who, you all know, are honorable men:
I will not do them wrong; I rather choose
To wrong the dead, to wrong myself and you,
Than I will wrong such honorable men.

42 B.C.

CLEOPATRA from ANTONY AND CLEOPATRA

by William Shakespeare

The barge she sat in, like a burnish'd throne,
Burn'd on the water. The poop was beaten gold;
Purple the sails, and so perfumed that
The winds were love-sick with them; the oars were silver,
Which to the tune of flutes kept stroke, and made
The water which they beat to follow faster,
As amorous of their strokes. For her own person,
It beggar'd all description: she did lie
In her pavilion—cloth-of-gold of tissue—
O'er-picturing that Venus where we see
The fancy outwork nature. On each side her
Stood pretty dimpled boys, like smiling Cupids,
With divers-color'd fans, whose wind did seem
To glow the delicate cheeks which they did cool,
And what they undid did.

AGRIPPA.   O! rare for Antony!

ENOBARBUS. Her gentlewomen, like the Nereides,
So many mermaids, tended her i' the eyes,
And made their bends adornings. At the helm
A seeming mermaid steers; the silken tackle
Swell with the touches of those flower-soft hands,
That yarely frame the office. From the barge
A strange invisible perfume hits the sense
Of the adjacent wharfs. The city cast
Her people out upon her; and Antony,
Enthroned i' the market-place, did sit alone,
Whistling to the air; which, but for vacancy,
Had gone to gaze on Cleopatra too
And made a gap in nature.

(51)

AGRIPPA.   Rare Egyptian!
ENOBARBUS.   Upon her landing, Antony sent to her,
  Invited her to supper. She replied,
  It should be better he became her guest;
  Which she entreated. Our courteous Antony,
  Whom ne'er the word of "No" woman heard speak,
  Being barbar'd ten times o'er, goes to the feast,
  And for his ordinary pays his heart
  For what his eyes eat only.
AGRIPPA.   Royal wench!
  She made great Caesar lay his sword to bed.
  He plough'd her and she cropp'd.
ENOBARBUS.   I saw her once
  Hop forty paces through the public street;
  And having lost her breath, she spoke, and panted,
  That she did make defect perfection,
  And, breathless, power breathe forth.
MECAENAS.   Now Antony must leave her utterly.
ENOBARBUS.   Never; he will not.
  Age cannot wither her, nor custom stale
  Her infinite variety. Other women cloy
  The appetites they feed, but she makes hungry
  Where most she satisfies; for vilest things
  Become themselves in her, that the holy priests
  Bless her when she is riggish.

A.D. 33

THE BALLAD OF THE GOODLY FERE

Simon Zelotes Speaketh It Somewhile After
The Crucifixion

by Ezra Pound

Ha' we lost the goodliest fere o' all
For the priests and the gallows tree?
Aye, lover he was of the brawney men,
O' ships and the open sea.

When they came wi' a host to take Our Man
His smile was good to see,
"First let these go!" quo' our Goodly Fere,
"Or I'll see ye damned," says he.

Aye, he sent us out through the crossed high spear
And the scorn of his laugh rang free,
"Why took ye not me when I walked about
Alone in the town?" says he.

Oh, we drank his "Hale" in the good red wine
When we last made company.
No capon priest was the Goodly Fere,
But a man o' men was he.

I ha' seen him drive a hundred men
Wi' a bundle o' cords swung free.
That they took the high and holy house
For their pawn and treasury.

(53)

They'll no get him a' in a book, I think,
Though they write it cunningly;
No mouse of the scrolls was the Goodly Fere
But aye loved the open sea.

If they think they ha' snared our Goodly Fere
They are fools to the last degree.
"I'll go to the feast," quo' our Goodly Fere,
"Though I go to the gallows tree."

"Ye ha' seen me heal the lame and blind,
And wake the dead," says he.
"Ye shall see one thing to master all:
'Tis how a brave man dies on the tree."

A son of God was the Goodly Fere
That bade his brothers be.
I ha' seen him cow a thousand men.
I have seen him on the tree.

He cried no cry when they drave the nails
And the blood gushed hot and free.
The hounds of the crimson sky gave tongue,
But never a cry cried he.

I ha' seen him cow a thousand men
On the hills o' Galilee.
They whined as he walked out calm between,
Wi' his eyes like the gray o' the sea.

Like the sea that brooks no voyaging,
With the winds unleashed and free,
Like the sea that he cowed at Genseret
Wi' twey words spoke suddenly.

A master of men was the Goodly Fere,
A mate of the wind and sea.
If they think they ha' slain our Goodly Fere
They are fools eternally.

I ha' seen him eat o' the honey-comb
Sin' they nailed him to the tree.

A.D. 61

BOADICEA

by *William Cowper*

When the British warrior Queen,
  Bleeding from the Roman rods,
Sought with an indignant mien,
  Counsel of her country's gods,

Sage beneath a spreading oak
  Sat the Druid, hoary chief,
Every burning word he spoke
  Full of rage, and full of grief:

"Princess! if our aged eyes
  Weep upon thy matchless wrongs,
'Tis because resentment ties
  All the terrors of our tongues.

"Rome shall perish—write that word
  In the blood that she has spilt;
Perish, hopeless and abhorr'd,
  Deep in ruin as in guilt.

"Rome, for empire far renown'd,
  Tramples on a thousand states;
Soon her pride shall kiss the ground—
  Hark! the Gaul is at her gates!

"Other Romans shall arise,
  Heedless of a soldier's name;
Sound, not arms, shall win the prize,
  Harmony the path to fame.

"Then the progeny that springs
   From the forests of our land,
Armed with thunder, clad with wings,
   Shall a wider world command.

"Regions Caesar never knew
   They posterity shall sway;
Where his eagles never flew,
   None invincible as they."

Such the bard's prophetic words,
   Pregnant with celestial fire,
Bending as he swept the chords
   Of his sweet but awful lyre.

She, with all a monarch's pride,
   Felt them in her bosom glow;
Rush'd to battle, fought and died;
   Dying, hurled them at the foe.

Ruffians, pitiless and proud
   Heaven awards the vengeance due;
Empire is on us bestowed,
   Shame and ruin wait for you!

❧

Under the Emperor Claudius, Rome consolidated the invasions of
Britain that had begun with Julius Caesar. Boadicea (now usually
spelled Boudicca) was queen of the Iceni, a British tribe, and led
a revolt against the Romans. After a few victories, she was defeated
and killed, but Cowper, writing from the eighteenth century, could
let his Druid priest predict the Decline and Fall of Rome and the
rise of the British Empire.

From *HYMN TO PROSERPINE*

(After the Proclamation in Rome of
the Christian Faith)

by *Algernon Charles Swinburne*

Vicisti, Galalaee

I have lived long enough, having seen one thing, that love hath
    an end;
Goddess and maiden and queen, be near me now and befriend.
Thou art more than the day or the morrow, the seasons that
    laugh or that weep;
For these give joy and sorrow; but thou, Proserpina, sleep.
Sweet is the treading of wine, and sweet the feet of the dove;
But a goodlier gift is thine than foam of the grapes or love.
Yea, is not even Apollo, with hair and harpstring of gold,
A bitter God to follow, a beautiful God to behold?
I am sick of singing: the bays burn deep and chafe; I am fain
To rest a little from praise and grievous pleasure and pain.
For the Gods we know not of, who give us our daily breath,
We know they are cruel as love or life, and lovely as death.
O Gods dethroned and deceased, cast forth, wiped out in a day!
From your wrath is the world released, redeemed from your
    chains, men say.
New Gods are crowned in the city, their flowers have broken
    your rods;
They are merciful, clothed with pity, the young compassionate
    Gods.
But for me their new device is barren, the days are bare;
Things long past over suffice, and men forgotten that were.
Time and the Gods are at strife; ye dwell in the midst thereof,
Draining a little life from the barren breasts of love.

(58)

I say to you, cease, take rest; yea, I say to you all, be at peace,
Till the bitter milk of her breast and the barren bosom shall cease.
Wilt thou yet take all, Galilean? But those thou shall not take,
The laurel, the palms, and the paean, the breasts of the nymphs
  in the brake;
Breasts more soft than a dove's, that tremble with tenderer
  breath;
And all the wings of the Loves, and all the joy before death;
All the feet of the hours that sound as a single lyre,
Dropped and deep in the flowers, with strings that flicker like fire.
More than these wilt thou give, things fairer than all these things?
Nay, for a little we live, and life hath mutable wings.
A little while and we die; shall life not thrive as it may?
For no man under the sky lives twice, outliving his day.
A grief is a grievous thing, and a man hath enough of his tears:
Why should he labor, and bring fresh grief to blacken his years?
Thou hast conquered, O pale Galilean; the world has grown gray
  from thy breath;
We have drunken of things Lethean, and fed on the fullness of
  death.
Laurel is green for a season, and love is sweet for a day;
But love grows bitter with treason, and laurel outlives not May.
Sleep, shall we sleep after all? For the world is not sweet in
  the end;
For the old faiths loosen and fall, the new years ruin and rend.
Fate is a sea without shore, and the soul is a rock that abides;
But her ears are vexed with the roar and her face with the foam
  of the tides.
O lips that the live blood faints in, the leavings of racks and rods!
O ghastly glories of saints, dead limbs of gibbeted Gods!
Though all men abuse them before you in spirit, and all knees
  bend,
I kneel not neither adore you, but standing, look to the end.

The old gods may have died in Rome in the third century, but Swinburne could write of them some 1,500 years later with a sharp and fresh nostalgia. Although Christianity was to prevail as the religion of all Europe and through the European-influenced world, the old gods held their firm footing from a base in Greek and Roman classics to influence literature for centuries longer.

A.D. 350

A SONG TO MITHRAS

(Hymn of the XXX Legion: circa A.D. 350)

by Rudyard Kipling

Mithras, God of the Morning, our trumpets waken the Wall!
"Rome is above the Nations, but Thou art over all!"
Now as the names are answered, and the guards are marched
    away,
Mithras, also a soldier, give us strength for the day!

Mithras, God of the Noontide, the heather swims in the heat.
Our helmets scorch our foreheads, our sandals burn our feet.
Now in the ungirt hour—now ere we blink and drowse,
Mithras, also a soldier, keep us true to our vows!

Mithras, God of the Sunset, low on the Western main—
Thou descending immortal, immortal to rise again!
Now when the watch is ended, now when the wine is drawn,
Mithras, also a soldier, keep us pure till the dawn!

Mithras, God of the Midnight, here where the great Bull dies,
Look on thy children in darkness. Oh, take our sacrifice!
Many roads thou hast fashioned—all of them lead to the Light!
Mithras, also a soldier, teach us to die aright!

❧

*Mithras was not exactly one of the old gods Swinburne mourned.
Mithraism came, like Christianity, from the East. It was originally a
Persian religion, brought West by the legions of the Caesars in the
second and third centuries. Its Bull God and secret rites seem to
have had wide appeal, especially among soldiers, and for a century*

or so it rivalled Christianity as the most popular new religion. Kipling's Roman legionaries are, of course, standing guard duty on the Great Wall built to keep the savage northern tribes from bothering Roman Britain.

A.D. 937

THE BATTLE OF BRUNANBURH

by Alfred, Lord Tennyson

Athelstan King,
Lord among Earls,
Bracelet-bestower and
Baron of Barons,
He with his brother,
Edmund Atheling,
Gaining a lifelong
Glory in battle,
Slew with the sword-edge
There by Brunanburh,
Brake the shield-wall,
Hew'd the lindenwood,
Hack'd the battleshield,
Sons of Edward with hammer'd brands.

We the West-Saxons,
Long as the daylight
Lasted, in companies
Troubled the track of the host that we hated,
Grimly with swords that were sharp from the grindstone,
Fiercely we hack'd at the flyers before us.

Five young kings put asleep by the sword stroke,
Seven strong Earls of the army of Anlaf
Fell on the war-field, numberless numbers,
Shipmen and Scotsmen.

Many a carcase they left to be carrion,
Many a livid one, many a sallow-skin—

Left for the white-tail'd eagle to tear it, and
Left for the horny-nibb'd raven to rend it, and
Gave to the garbaging war-hawk to gorge it, and
That gray beast, the wolf of the weald.

❧

Athelstan, or Ethelstand, a grandson of the legendary King Alfred,
held his inherited island empire together against both raids from the
Northmen and an attempted Scottish revolt recorded above.

A.D. 950

WAR SONG OF THE SARACENS

by James Elroy Flecker

We are they who come faster than fate: we are they who ride
early or late:
We storm at your ivory gate: Pale Kings of the Sunset, beware!
Not on silk nor in samet we lie, not in curtain'd solemnity die
Among women who chatter and cry, and children who mumble
a prayer.
But we sleep by the ropes of the camp, and we rise with a shout,
and we tramp
With the sun or the moon for a lamp, and the spray of the wind
in our hair.

From the lands where the elephants are, to the forts of Meron
and Balghar,
Our steel we have brought and our star to shine on the ruins
of Rûm.
We have marched from the Indus to Spain, and by God we will
go there again;
We have stood on the shore of the plain where the Waters of
Destiny boom.
A mart of destruction we made at Jalula where men were afraid,
For death was a difficult trade, and the sword was a broker
of doom;

And the Spear was a Desert Physician who cured not a few of
ambition,
And drave not a few to perdition with medicine bitter and strong:
And the shield was a brief to the fool and as bright as a desolate
pool,

And as straight as the rock of Stamboul when their cavalry
    thunder'd along:
For the coward was drown'd with the brave when our battle
    sheered up like a wave,
And the dead to the desert we gave, and their glory to God in
    our song.

      ❦

If Mithraism was completely absorbed and replaced by Christianity,
the next Eastern faith, founded in 612 by Muhammad, its Prophet,
was to prove more enduring. Islam, confined at its beginning to a
handful of Hashimite Arabs around Mecca and Medina, exploded
across the map to cover all Arabia, much of Persia and India, North
Africa, Spain, and other enclaves in Southern Europe in less than a
hundred and fifty years. Christian soldiers stopped it, roughly in a
line splitting the Mediterranean and then curving higher above Turkey and Persia, in battles from Tours (732) to the Black Sea, but the
wave could never be rolled back. Today Islam claims some 500 million followers to Christianity's 950 million.

A.D. 1030

A FACT, AND AN IMAGINATION
or, Canute and Alfred, on the Seashore

by William Wordsworth

I

The Danish Conqueror, on his royal chair,
Mustering a face of haughty sovreignty,
To aid a covert purpose, cried—"O ye
Approaching waters of the deep, that share
With this green isle my fortunes, come not where
Your Master's throne is set."—Deaf was the Sea;
Her waves rolled on, respecting his decree
Less than they heed a breath of wanton air.
—Then Canute, rising from his invaded throne,
Said to his servile Courtiers,—"Poor the reach.
The undisguised extent, of mortal sway!
He only is a King, and he alone
Deserves the name (this truth the billows preach)
Whose everlasting laws, sea, earth, and heaven, obey."

II

This just reproof the prosperous Dane
Drew, from the influx of the main,
For some whose rugged northern mouths would strain
At oriental flattery;
And Canute (fact more worthy to be known)
From that time forth did for his brows disown
The ostentatious symbol of a crown;
Esteeming earthly royalty
Contemptible as vain.

(67)

Now hear what one of elder days,
Rich theme of England's fondest praise,
Her darling Alfred *might* have spoken;
To cheer the remnant of his host
When he was driven from coast to coast,
Distressed and harassed, but with mind unbroken:

III

"My faithful followers, lo! the tide is spent
That rose, and steadily advanced to fill
The shores and channels, working Nature's will
Among the mazy streams that backward went,
And in the sluggish pits where ships are pent:
And now, his task performed, the flood stands still,
At the green base of many an island hill,
In placid beauty and sublime content!
Such the repose that sage and hero find;
Such measured rest the sedulous and the good
Of humbler name; whose souls do, like the flood
Of Ocean, press right on; or gently wind,
Neither to be diverted nor withstood,
Until they reach the bounds by Heaven assigned."

❧

Canute, either to shame sycophantic courtiers or from an overweening notion of his own power, is supposed to have commanded the
sea to stand still; it didn't. Wordsworth picks up the anecdote to
provide an imaginary contrast with what King Alfred might have said
in a similar situation. Alfred the Great had reigned from 871 to 901.
Canute ruled Denmark, Norway, and England, but his heirs let
English power pass back to Edward the Confessor (1042-1066).

A.D. 1066

From *THE TRUE-BORN ENGLISHMAN*

by *Daniel Defoe*

The Romans first with *Julius Caesar* came,
Including all the Nations of that Name,
Gauls, Greeks, and *Lombards:* and by Computation,
Auxiliaries of Slaves of ev'ry Nation.
With *Hengist, Saxons: Danes* with *Sueno* came,
In search of Plunder, not in search of Fame.
Scots, Picts, and *Irish* from th' *Hibernian* Shore:
And Conqu'ring *William* brought the *Normans* o'er.
    All these their Barb'rous offspring left behind,
The Dregs of Armies, they of all Mankind;
Blended with *Britains* who before were here,
Of whom the *Welsh* ha' blessed the Character.
    From this Amphibious Ill-born Mob began
That vain ill-natured thing, an Englishman.
The Customs, Sirnames, Languages, and Manners,
Of all these Nations are their own Explainers:
Whose Relicks are so lasting and so strong,
They ha' left a *Shiboleth* upon our Tongue;
By which with easy search you may distinguish
Your *Roman-Saxon-Danish-Norman* English.
    The great Invading *Norman* let us know
What Conquerors in After-Times might do.
To ev'ry *Musqueteer* he brought to Town,
He gave the lands which never were his own.
When first the *English* Crown he did obtain,
He did not send his *Dutchmen* home again.
No Reassumptions in his Reign were known,
Davenant might there ha' let his Book alone.
No Parliament his Army could disband:

He rais'd no Money, for he paid in Land.
He gave his Legions their Eternal Station,
And made them all Freeholders of the Nation.
He canton'd out the Country to his Men,
And ev'ry Soldier was a Denizen.
The Rascals thus enrich'd he call'd them *Lords*,
To please their Upstart Pride with new-made Words;
And *Doomsday Book* his Tyranny Records.

    And here begins the Ancient Pedigree
That so exalts our Poor Nobility:
'Tis that from some *French* Trooper they derive,
Who with the *Norman* Bastard did arrive:
The Trophies of the Families appear;
Some show the Sword, the Bow, and some the Spear,
Which their Great Ancestor, *forsooth*, did wear.
These in the Heralds Register remain,
Their Noble mean Extraxtion to explain.
Yet who the Hero was, no Man can tell,
Whether a Drummer or a Colonel:
The silent Record blushes to reveal
Their Undescended Dark Original.

    But grant the best, How came the Change to pass;
A *True-Born Englishman* of *Norman* Race?
A Turkish Horse can show more History,
To prove his Well-descended Family.
Conquest, as by the Moderns 'tis exprest,
May give a title to the lands possest:
But that the Longest Sword shou'd be so Civil,
To make a *Frenchman English*, that the Devil.

    These are the Heroes who despise the *Dutch*,
And rail at new-come Foreigners so much;
Forgetting that themselves are all deriv'd
From the most Scoundrel Race that ever liv'd,
A horrid Crowd of Rambling Thieves and Drones,
Who ransack'd Kingdoms, and dispeopled Towns:

The *Pict* and Painted *Britain,* Treach'rous *Scot,*
By Hunger, Theft, and Rapine, hither brought;
Norwegian Pirates, Buccaneering *Danes,*
Whose Red-hair'd Offspring ev'ry where remains;
Who join'd with *Norman-French* compound the Breed
From whence your *True-Born Englishmen* proceed.

❦

Harold the Saxon, descended from Jutes, Danes, and almost anyone
else you care to mention, was legally chosen king of England by a
council of nobles. But William the Bastard of Normandy had earlier
forced Harold to vow to help him (William) get the crown. William
was quick to remind Harold of this promise, but Harold was not ready
to honor it. Harold might have held the kingship, but too many
things happened at once. Tostig and Haardraade, the one a rebellious
English earl, the other king of Norway, landed with an army in the
north. Harold defeated them at the Battle of Stamford Bridge, but
at the same time William's Norman invasion had begun to move
toward the south. Himself and his army exhausted from the first
battle, Harold rushed to meet the Normans at Hastings or Senlac
where he lost his life and the crown he had worn for less than a year.
And Defoe's True-Born Englishman was launched upon the island,
and the world.

A.D. 1087

THE CID'S RISING

by Felicia Hemans

'Twas the deep mid-watch of the silent night,
 And Leon in slumber lay,
When a sound went forth in rushing might,
 Like an army on its way!
 In the stillness of the hour,
 When the dreams of sleep have power,
  And men forget the day.

Through the dark and lonely streets it went,
 Till the slumberers woke in dread;—
The sound of a passing armament,
 With the charger's stony tread.
 There was heard no trumpet's peal,
 But the heavy tramp of steel,
  As a host's to combat led.

Through the dark and lonely streets it pass'd,
 And the hollow pavement rang,
And the towers, as with a sweeping blast,
 Rock'd to the stormy clang!
 But the march of the viewless train
 Went on to a royal fane,
  Where a priest his night-hymn sang.

There was knocking that shook the marble floor,
 And a voice at the gate, which said—
"That the Cid Ruy Diez, the Campeador,
 Was there in his arms array'd;
 And that with him, from the tomb,

Had the Count Gonzalez come
    With a host, uprisen to aid!

"And they came for the buried king that lay
    At rest in that ancient fame;
For he must be arm'd on the battle-day,
    With them, to deliver Spain!"
—Then the march went sounding on,
And the Moors, by noontide sun,
    Were dust on Tolosa's plain.

❦

The Cid, Rodrigo Díaz, was a slippery Castilian mercenary soldier who fought on both Spanish Christian and on Islamic sides in the long battle for consolidation of a Spanish nation. Despite this record, he has been enshrined as the national hero of (Christian) Spain. Legend has it that, for his last great battle, his wife clothed his dead body in his familiar armor and set it on horseback to inspire the Spanish forces.

From CRUSADER CHORUS

by Charles Kingsley

(Men-at-Arms pass, singing)

The tomb of God before us,
Our fatherland behind,
Our ships shall leap o'er billows steep,
Before a charmèd wind.

Above our van great angels
Shall fight along the sky;
While martyrs pure and crowned saints
To God for rescue cry.

The red-cross knights and yeomen
Throughout the holy town,
In fate and might, on left and right,
Shall tread the paynim down.

Till on the Mount Moriah
The Pope of Rome shall stand;
The Kaiser and the King of France
Shall guard him on each hand.

There shall he rule all nations,
With crozier and with sword;
And pour on all the heathen
The wrath of Christ the Lord.

(Women-bystanders)

Christ is a rock in the bare salt land,
To shelter our knights from the sun and sand:

Christ the Lord is a summer sun,
To ripen the grain while they are gone . . .

(Old Knights pass)

Our stormy sun is sinking;
Our sands are running low;
In one fair fight, before the night,
Our hard-worn hearts shall glow.

We cannot pine in cloister;
We cannot fast and pray;
The sword which built our load of guilt
Must wipe that guilt away.

We know the doom before us;
The dangers of the road;
Have mercy, mercy, Jesu blest,
When we lie low in blood . . .

(Boy-Crusaders pass)

The Christ-child sits on high:
He looks through the merry blue sky;
He holds in his hand a bright lily-band,
For the boys who for Him die . . .

(Young Knights pass)

The rich East blooms fragrant before us;
All Fairy-land beckons us forth;
We must follow the crane in her flight o'er the main,
From the frosts and the moors of the North.

Our sires in the youth of the nations
Swept westward through plunder and blood,

(75)

But a holier quest calls us back to the East,
We fight for the kingdom of God . . .

(Old Monk, looking after them)

Jerusalem, Jerusalem!
The burying place of God!
Why gay and bold, in steel and gold,
O'er the paths where Christ hath trod?

❧

The Crusades were a fantastic combination of politics, greed, devotion, high idealism, and raw brutality. Their original and continuing
purpose was to reclaim the Holy Land, where Jesus had walked and
taught, from possession of the infidel Islamic rule. But, for over two
hundred years, the holy cause was diverted and twisted to allow for
dynastic struggles between Christian leaders, to buttress the power
of the Papacy against that of only nominally subject kings and for
shameless looting by noble and base Crusaders alike. Jerusalem was
reclaimed and held for a short time and Arabia today is still dotted
with ruins of Crusader castles which held out as independent prin-
cipalities long after the true crusades had withered away in the thir-
teenth century.

c. A.D. 1190

From *THE SONG OF IGOR'S CAMPAIGN*

translated by Vladimir Nabokov

IGOR'S ESCAPE

Meanwhile, like an ermine,
Igor has sped to the reeds,
and [settled] upon the water
like a white duck.
He leapt upon the swift steed,
and sprang off it,
[and ran on], like a demon wolf,
and sped to the meadowland of the Donets,
and, like a falcon,
flew up to the mists,
killing geese
and swans,
for lunch,
and for dinner,
and for supper.

And even as Igor, like a falcon, flew,
Vlur, like a wolf, sped,
shaking off by his passage the cold dew;
for both had worn out
their swift steeds.
Says the Donets:
"Prince Igor!
Not small is your magnification,
and Konchak's detestation,
and the Russian land's gladness."

Igor says:
"O Donets!
Not small is *your* magnification:
you it was who lolled
a prince on [your] waves;
who carpeted for him
with green grass
your silver banks;
who clothed him
with warm mists
under the shelter of the green tree;
who had him guarded
by the golden-eye on the water,
the gulls on the currents,
the [crested] black ducks on the winds.

❧

Igor was a semi-legendary Russian prince in the shadowy years when
Russia was still in the process of emerging as a recognizable nation.
He fought against the Tatars with intermittent success. The Donets
is the Don River.

THE REEDS OF RUNNYMEDE

(Magna Charta, June 15, 1215)

by Rudyard Kipling

At Runnymede, at Runnymede,
  What say the reeds at Runnymede?
The lissom reeds that give and take,
That bend so far, but never break.
They keep the sleepy Thames awake
  With tales of John at Runnymede.

At Runnymede, at Runnymede,
  Oh, hear the reeds at Runnymede:—
"You mustn't sell, delay, deny,
A freeman's right or liberty,
It wakes the stubborn Englishry,
  We saw 'em roused at Runnymede.

"When through our ranks the Barons came,
With little thought of praise or blame,
But resolute to play the game,
  They lumbered up to Runnymede;
And there they launched in solid line,
The first attack on Right Divine—
The curt, uncompromising 'Sign!'
  That settled John at Runnymede.

"At Runnymede, at Runnymede,
Your rights were won at Runnymede!
No freeman shall be fined or bound,
  Or dispossessed of freehold ground,
Except by lawful judgement found

And passed upon him by his peers.
Forget not, after all these years,
    The Charter signed at Runnymede."

And still when Mob or Monarch lays
Too rude a hand on English ways,
The whisper wakes, the shudder plays,
    Across the reeds at Runnymede.
And Thames, that knows the moods of kings,
And crowds and priests and suchlike things,
Rolls deep and dreadful as he brings
    Their warning down from Runnymede.

❧

The Barons of England, joined by the powerful Archbishop Stephen
Langton and with much popular feeling on their side, forced King
John to concede certain well-understood but never previously docu-
mented rights to all freemen of England. The Great Charter that
John signed at Runnymede on the Thames still stands as one of the
firm bases of English law. The whole affair served to place the king in
history as Bad King John. Actually, he was a rather capable and con-
cientious administrator for his time, doing the hard work while his
grand-standing brother, Richard the Lion-hearted, milked the public
treasury to finance his crusading ventures.

A.D. 1282

THE FALL OF LLYWELYN, THE LAST WELSH PRINCE

by Beddyn Fardd

translated by D. M. Lloyd

Great Christ, generous Lord, a grace I seek,
Christ Son of God, the guileless One, forget not me,
The righteous, gift-bearing Christ, most powerful Surety,
Whose body bore the keenest pain.

What I relate concerns a man.
He who endures grief may he be the most calm.
He who is endowed with the highest power
May his mind be the lowliest.

Christ came to the world so that Adam
And his people should not be in Hell, an enslaved multitude,
And to people heaven around the Exalted Lord,
Which was lost by that most purblind angel.

Great Wales has lost the manliest of leaders,
Brave his sword-blade, active, splendidly brave and most valiant
    was he;
A courageous leader no longer lives, how shall I endure his loss?—
Brave and manly, generous, most free bestower of gifts.

It was for us that this man was killed, this man who was supreme,
A man who ruled Wales, boldly I will name him:
Valiant Llywelyn, the bravest of Welshmen,
A man who loved not to slink into the easiest way out.

(81)

A strong man in the attack on a host on his border,
A man of the green tents, the maintainer of the camp,
Manly son of Gruffudd, most ungrasping giver of largesse
In the splendid tradition of Nudd and Mordaf.

A red-speared man, a man grief-stricken like Priam,
A fine man as king over the proudest army,
A man whose fame will spread easily—most generous his outlay—
As far as the sun travels on his farthest course.

It is a grievous thing that that man is destroyed, a most courtly
  leader,
A man bitterly mourned, the truest of kinsmen,
A refined, wise, and upright man, the best from Anglesey
To Caerleon, that fairest of places.

Llywelyn who stood near the linits of the Taff,
A leader of the people, lavish bestower of raiment.
A man far above them all, the greatest of soldiers,
As far as Porth Wygyr a calm eagle.

May He who bore the direst and most painful death
For the sake of the five ages of the world, the heaviest and most
  grievous agonies,
May He receive my most noble and gentle prince
To his portion of mercy, which is the greatest of greatnesses.

❧

England, now become a real nation, proved she could be as ruthless
as the Romans who had long before oppressed her. Edward I took
his army into Wales to quell a local separatist rebellion. He killed
Llywelyn and brought home with him the Welsh longbow, a weapon
which was to turn the tide for English victories against France in
years to come.

(82)

A.D. 1314

SCOTS, WHA HAE

by Robert Burns

Scots, wha hae wi' Wallace bled,
Scots wham Bruce has aften led,
Welcome to your gory bed
    Or to victory!

Now's the day, and now's the hour:
See the front o' battle lour,
See approach proud Edward's power—
    Chains and slaverie!

Wha will be a traitor knave?
Wha can fill a coward's grave?
Wha sae base as be a slave?—
    Let him turn and flee!

Wha for Scotland's King and Law
Freedom's sword will strongly draw,
Freeman stand, or freeman fa',
    Let him follow me!

By Oppression's woes and pains,
By your sons in servile chains,
We will draw our dearest veins
    But they shall be free!

Lay the proud usurpers low!
Tyrants fall in every foe!
Liberty's in every blow!
    Let us do, or die!

(83)

Edward II had less luck against the warlike Scots. At Bannockburn, Robert Bruce defeated an English army and established an independent Scotland that would last some 200 years until the Scots king, James VI became James I of England. Wallace had been the great Scots leader of a generation earlier, executed by Edward I.

A.D. 1330

TO THE GUELF FACTION

by Folgore da San Geminiano

translated by DANTE GABRIEL ROSSETTI

Because ye made your backs your shields, it came
  To pass, ye Guelfs, that these your enemies
  From hares grew lions: and because your eyes
Turn'd homeward, and your spurs e'en did the same,
Full many an one who still might win the game
  In fever'd tracts of exile pines and dies.
  Ye blew your bubbles as the falcon flies,
And the wind broke them up and scatter'd them.
This counsel, therefore. Shape your high resolves
  In good King Robert's humor, and afresh
    Accept your shames, forgive, and go your way,
  And so her peace is made with Pisa! Yea
  What cares she for the miserable flesh
That in the wilderness has fed the wolves?

✿

The Guelfs (and their rivals, the Ghibellines) were latinizations of
Welf and *Waiblinger*, two German factions whose struggles lasted
through generations of strife from Saxony down through the Italian
boot. In these long centuries after the Fall of the Roman Empire,
Italy was a crazy-quilt pattern of small states run for profit and
prestige by native or invading princes. Robert of Naples was a leader
of the Italian Guelfs in the fourteenth century. The name has hung
on long after, and when George I came to rule England from his
German seat at Hanover, his adherents were nicknamed Guelfs—a
semantic return from the Italian of their family *Welf* affiliation.

A.D. 1350

PROTUS

by Robert Browning

Among these latter busts we count by scores,
Half-emperors and quarter-emperors,
Each with his bay-leaf fillet, loose-thonged vest,
Loric and low-browed Gorgon on the breast,—
One loves a baby face, with violets there,
Violets instead of laurel in the hair,
As those were all the little locks could bear.

Now read here. "Protus ends a period
Of empery beginning with a god;
Born in the porphyry chamber at Byzant,
Queens by his cradle, proud and ministrant:
And if he quickened breath there, 'twould like fire
Pantingly through the dim vast realm transpire.

A fame that he was missing spread afar—
The world, from its four corners, rose in war,
Till he was borne out on a balcony
To pacify the world when it should see.
The captains ranged before him, one, his hand
Made baby points at, gained the chief command.
And day by day more beautiful he grew
In shape, all said, in feature, and in hue,
While young Greek sculptors gazing on the child,
Became, with old Greek sculpture, reconciled.
Already sages labored to condense
In easy tomes a life's experience:
And artists took grave counsel to impart
In one breath and one hand-sweep, all their art—

To make his graces prompt as blossoming
Of plentifully-watered palms in spring:
Since well beseems it, whoso mounts the throne,
For beauty, knowledge, strength, should stand alone,
And mortals love the letters of his name."

—Stop! Have you turned two pages? Still the same,
New reign, same date. The scribe goes on to say
How that same year, on such a month and day,
"John the Pannonian, groundedly believed
A blacksmith's bastard, whose hard hand reprieved
The Empire from its fate the year before,—
Came, had a mind to take the crown, and wore
The same for six years (during which the Huns
Kept off their fingers from us), till his sons
Put something in his liquor"—and so forth.
Then a new reign. Stay—"Take at its just worth"
(Subjoins an annotator) "what I give
As hearsay. Some think, John let Protus live
And slip away. 'Tis said, he reached man's age
At some blind northern court; made, first a page,
Then, tutor to the children; last, of use
About the hunting-stables. I deduce
He wrote the little tract 'On worming dogs,'
Whereof the name in sundry catalogues
Is extant yet. A Protus of the race
Is rumored to have died a monk in Thrace,—
And if the same, he reached senility."

Here's John the Smith's rough-hammered head. Great eye,
Gross jaw and griped lips to what granite can
To give you the crown-grasper. What a man!

❧

I cannot find Browning's Protus under that name in any list of either Roman or Byzantian emperors, but he could easily be one of the ones named Phocas. Whatever, the verses do give an evocative capsule of the total confusion of the Eastern Empire, sheared off from Rome at the Fall, looted as much by its own greedy rulers as by marauding Saracens and uninvited Crusader guests. Vast wealth, decadence and political corruption gave this segment of the Near East—Turkey and environs—a reputation for double-dealing that has lived until the present. Assassination, discreet poisoning, capture of the throne by anyone strong enough to hold it for a few years (blacksmith's bastard or cunning counsellor) were common.

From *TAMBURLAINE*

by *Christopher Marlowe*

TAMBURLAINE:
And ride in triumph through Persepolis!—
Is it not brave to be a king, Techelles!—
Usumcasane and Theridamas,
Is it not passing brave to be a king,
And ride in triumph through Persepolis?

TECHELLES:
O my lord, it is sweet and full of pomp!

USUMCASANE:
To be a king, is half to be a god.

TAMBURLAINE:
A god is not so glorious as a king:
I think the pleasures they enjoy in heaven,
Cannot compare with kingly joys in earth;—
To wear a crown enchas'd with pearl and gold,
Whose virtues carry with it life and death;
To ask and have, command and be obey'd;
When looks breed love, with looks to gain the prize,
Such power attractive shines in princes' eyes.

❦

Tamburlaine, Tamerlane, Timur—he has half a dozen spellings—
the rude Mongol who first overthrew his master Chagatay Khan and
then quickly moved south-east to conquer Afghanistan, Persia, and
Mesopotamia. His dynasty and power did not long survive his death in

1405, but his name remained to inspire a young English poet, Christopher Marlowe, who almost single-handedly invented a new verse form, the resounding line of unrhymed pentameter which was to find fullest glory in its adoption by Shakespeare.

AGINCOURT

by Michael Drayton

Fair stood the wind for France
When we our sails advance;
Nor now to prove our chance
    Longer will tarry;
But putting to the main,
At Caux, the mouth of Seine,
With all his martial train
    Landed King Harry.

And taking many a fort,
Furnished in warlike sort,
Marcheth towards Agincourt
    In happy hour;
Skirmishing day by day
With those that stopped his way,
Where the French general lay
    With all his power.

Which, in his height of pride,
King Henry to deride,
His ransom to provide
    To the King sending;
Which he neglects the while,
As from a nation vile,
Yet with an angry smile
    Their fall portending.

And turning to his men,
Quoth our brave Harry then:

"Though they to one be ten
      Be not amazèd!
Yet have we well begun:
Battles so bravely won
Have ever to the sun
      By Fame been raisèd!

"And for myself," quoth he
"This my full rest shall be:
England ne'er mourn for me,
      Nor more esteem me!
Victor I will remain,
Or on this earth lie slain;
Never shall She sustain
      Loss to redeem me.

"Poitiers and Cressy tell
When most their pride did swell,
Under our sword they fell.
      No less our skill is,
Than when our Grandsire great,
Claiming the regal seat,
By many a warlike feat
      Lopped the French lilies."

The Duke of York so dread
The eager vanguard led;
With the main, Henry sped,
      Amongst his henchmen.
Exeter had the rear,
A braver man not there!
O Lord how hot they were
      On the false Frenchman!

They now to fight are gone;
Armor on armor shone;
Drum now to drum did groan:
    To hear, was wonder;
That, with the cries they make,
The very earth did shake;
Trumpet to trumpet spake;
    Thunder to thunder.

Well it thine age became,
O noble Erpingham,
Which didst the signal aim
    To our hid forces!
When, from a meadow by,
Like a storm suddenly,
The English archery
    Stuck the French horses.

With Spanish yew so strong;
Arrows a cloth-yard long,
That like to serpents stung,
    Piercing the weather.
None from his fellow starts;
But, playing many parts,
And like true English hearts,
    Stuck close together.

When down their bows they threw,
And forth their bilboes drew,
And on the French they flew:
    Not one was tardy.
Arms were from shoulders sent,
Scalps to the teeth were rent,
Down the French peasants went:
    Our men were hardy.

(93)

This while our noble King,
His broad sword brandishing,
Down the French host did sing,
    As to o'erwhelm it;
And many a deep wound lent;
His arms with blood besprent,
And many a cruel dent
    Bruised his helmet.

Gloucester, that duke so good,
Next of the royal blood,
For famous England stood
    With his brave brother;
Clarence, in steel so bright,
Though but a maiden knight,
Yet in that furious fight
    Scarce such another!

Warwick in blood did wade,
Oxford, the foe invade,
And cruel slaughter made,
    Still as they ran up.
Suffolk his axe did ply;
Beaumont and Willoughby
Bare them right doughtily;
    Ferrers and Fanhope.

Upon Saint Crispin's Day
Fought was this noble Fray,
Which Fame did not delay
    To England to carry.
Oh, when shall English men
With such acts fill a pen?
Or England breed again
    Such a King Harry?

Henry V of England, his army well-supplied with those longbows (shooting cloth-yard arrows) his grandsire Edward had discovered in Wales, vanquished a French army three times the size of his and temporarily won back much of the Norman land England still claimed.

From HENRY VI, PART I

by William Shakespeare

BASTARD: (to CHARLES, the Dolphin)
Methinks your looks are sad, your cheer appall'd.
Hath the late overthrow wrought this offence?
Be not dismay'd, for succour is at hand:
A holy maid hither with me I bring,
Which by a vision sent to her from heaven
Ordained is to raise this tedious siege
And drive the English forth the bounds of France.
The spirit of deep prophecy she hath,
Exceeding the nine Sibyls of old Rome:
What's past and what's to come she can descry.
Speak, shall I call her in? Believe my words,
For they are certain, and unfallible.

CHARLES:
Go, call her in. (Exit Bastard) But first, to try her skill,
Reignier, stand thou as Dolphin in my place:
Question her proudly; let thy looks be stern:
By this means shall we sound what skill she hath.

Enter Joan La Puzell

REIGNIER:
Fair Maid, is't thou wilt do these wondrous feats?

JOAN:
Reignier, is't thou that thinkest to beguile me?
Where is the Dolphin? Come, come from behind,
I know thee well, though never seen before.

Be not amazed, there's nothing hid from me:
In private will I talk to thee apart.
Stand back, you lords, and give us leave awhile.

REIGNIER:
She takes upon her bravely at first dash.

JOAN:
Dolphin, I am by birth a shepherd's daughter,
My wit untrain'd in any kind of art.
Heaven and our Lady gracious hath it pleased
To shine on my contemptible estate.
Lo, while I waited on my tender lambs,
And to sun's parching heat display'd my cheeks,
God's mother deigned to appear to me,
And in a vision full of majesty,
Will'd me to leave my base vocation,
And free my country from calamity:
Her aid she promised, and assured success:
In complete glory she reveal'd herself;
And, whereas I was black and swart before,
With those clear rays which she infused on me
That beauty I am bless'd with which you see.
Ask me what question thou canst possible,
And I will answer unpremeditated:
My courage try by combat, if thou darest,
And thou shalt find that I exceed my sex.
Resolve on this, thou shalt be fortunate,
If thou receive me for thy warlike mate.

CHARLES:
Thou hast astonish'd me with thy high terms:
Only this proof I'll of thy valour make,
In single combat thou shalt buckle with me;

(97)

And if thou vanquishest, thy words are true;
Otherwise I renounce all confidence.

JOAN:
I am prepared: here is my keen-edged sword,
Deck'd with five flower-de-luces on each side;
The which at Touraine, in Saint Katharine's churchyard,
Out of a great deal of old iron, I chose forth.

CHARLES:
Then come, o' God's name; I fear no woman.

JOAN:
And while I live, I'll ne'er fly from a man.

Here they fight, and Joan La Puzell overcomes.

CHARLES:
Stay, stay thy hands! thou art an Amazon
And fightest with the sword of Deborah.

JOAN:
Christ's mother helps me, else I were too weak.

CHARLES:
Whoe'er helps thee, 'tis thou that must help me:
Impatiently I burn with thy desire:
My heart and hands thou hast at once subdued.
Excellent Puzell, if thy name be so,
Let me thy servant, and not sovereign be,
'Tis the French Dolphin sueth to thee thus.

I must not yield to any rites of love,
For my profession's sacred from above:

(98)

When I have chased all thy foes from hence,
Then will I think upon a recompense.

Agincourt by no means ended the English-French wars; they were to continue, off and on, for another four hundred years. The French side received unexpected aid during the siege of Orleans when Jeanne d'Arc, a simple peasant girl inspired by heavenly visions, joined them. Charles VII (still called the Dauphin—Shakespeare's Dolphin—since he had not yet been crowned) accepted her aid. She helped lift the siege, but was captured by the British the next year. Charles, with royal gratitude, did not interfere when she was tried as a witch and burned at Rouen in 1431.

Puzell = *Pucelle, La Pucelle being an alternate name for Jeanne d'Arc.*

A.D. 1431

PIBROCH OF DONUIL DHU

by Sir Walter Scott

Pibroch of Donuil Dhu,
  Pibroch of Donuil,
Wake thy wild voice anew,
  Summon Clan-Conuil.
Come away, come away,
  Hark to the summons!
Come in your war array,
  Gentles and commons.

Come from deep glen, and
  From mountain so rocky,
The war-pipe and pennon
  Are at Inverlochy.
Come every hill-plaid, and
  True heart that wears one,
Come every steel blade, and
  Strong hand that bears one.

Leave untended the herd,
  The flock without shelter;
Leave the corpse uninterr'd,
  The bride at the altar;
Leave the deer, leave the steer,
  Leave nets and barges:
Come with your fighting gear,
  Broadswords and targes.

Come as the winds come, when
  Forests are rended,

Come as the waves come, when
    Navies are stranded:
Faster come, faster come
    Faster and faster,
Chief, vassal, page and groom,
    Tenant and master.

Fast they come, fast they come;
    See how they gather!
Wild waves the eagle plume,
    Blended with heather.
Cast your plaids, draw your blades,
    Forward, each man, set!
Pibroch of Donuil Dhu,
    Knell for the onset!

The Scots fought one another, tribe against tribe, tartan against tartan, with as much avidity as they opposed England. According to Scott, this song celebrates an expedition of the Clan MacDonald against the Earls of Mar and Caithness at Inverlochy. A pibroch is a tune played on the bagpipe, can refer to the pipe itself.

A.D. 1485

From RICHARD III

by William Shakespeare

The Field at Bosworth

(*King Richard is addressing his nobles and his army*)

KING RICHARD:
Go, gentlemen, every man unto his charge:
(*Aside*) Let not our babbling dreams affright our souls:
Conscience is but a word that cowards use,
Devised at first to keep the strong in awe:
Our strong arms be our conscience, swords our law.
(*To them*) March on, join bravely, let us to't pell-mell;
If not to heaven, then hand in hand to hell.

His oration to his army

What shall I say more than I have inferr'd?
Remember whom you are to cope withal;
A sort of vagabonds, rascals, and runaways,
A scum of Britains, and base lackey peasants,
Whom their o'er-cloyed country vomits forth
To desperate ventures and assured destruction.
You sleeping safe, they bring you to unrest;
You having lands, and blest with beauteous wives,
They would restrain the one, distain the other.
And who doth lead them but a paltry fellow,
Long kept in Britain at our mother's cost?
A milksop, one that never in his life
Felt so much cold as over shoes in snow?

Let's whip these stragglers o'er the seas again;
Lash hence these overweening rags of France,
These famish'd beggars weary of their lives,
Who, but for dreaming on this fond exploit,
For want of means, poor rats, had hang'd themselves:
If we be conquer'd, let men conquer us,
And not these bastard Britains, whom our fathers
Have in their own land beaten, bobb'd, and thump'd,
And in record, left them the heirs of shame.
Shall these enjoy our lands? lie with our wives?
Ravish our daughters? (*Drum afar off*) Hark! I hear their drum.
Fight! gentlemen of England! fight, bold yeomen!
Draw, archers, draw your arrows to the head!
Sour your proud horses hard, and ride in blood!
Amaze the welkin with your broken staves!

    Enter a Messenger

What says Lord Stanley? will he bring his power?

MESSENGER:
My lord, he doth deny to come.

KING RICHARD:
Off with his son George's head!

NORFOLK:
My lord, the enemy is past the marsh:
After the battle let George Stanley die.

KING RICHARD:
A thousand hearts are great within my bosom:
Advance our standards, set upon our foes;
Our ancient word of courage, fair Saint George,

    (*103*)

Inspire us with the spleen of fiery dragons!
Upon them! Victory sits on our helms.

Exeunt

Alarum; excursions. Enter Catesby.

CATESBY:
Rescue, my Lord of Norfolk, rescue, rescue!
The King enacts more wonders than a man,
Daring an opposite to every danger:
His horse is slain, and all on foot he fights,
Seeking for Richmond in the throat of death.
Rescue, fair lord, or else the day is lost!

Alarums. Enter King Richard

KING RICHARD:
A horse! a horse! my kingdom for a horse!

CATESBY:
Withdraw, my lord; I'll help you to a horse.

KING RICHARD:
Slave, I have set my life upon a cast
And I will stand the hazard of the die:
I think there be six Richmonds in the field;
Five have I slain today instead of him.
A horse! a horse! my kingdom for a horse!

Exeunt

*Alarum. Enter King Richard and Richmond; they fight;
Richard is slain.*

(104)

According to historical records, Richard Crookback was a fairly good king for his short reign. But the literary record, stemming first from the writings of Sir Thomas More, a propagandist for Richard's enemies, the Plantagenet rulers who took over the throne, second from Shakespeare, paints him as a hideous villain and child-murderer. Yet even Shakespeare couldn't forbear giving him a battle-finish of some heroism.

A.D. 1492

THE NIGHT BEFORE AMERICA

by Norma Farber

All the night they heard birds passing,
navigating air south-westward,
flying wing-routes into darkness,
over the slack and strain of rigging,
over the faint-hearts, over the night-fears,
over the Admiral Don Cristóbal
pledged to land, island or mainland,
four weeks out of sight of *tierra*,
thirty days out of Canaries
into the predicate of westward,
Indies, westward into the Indies,
goal of the keel, clue to the voyage,
purpose of helm, the sail's finale,
all through darkness, *toda la noche*
sound of flyways flapping arrival,
fledging closer to coastal country
tremulous with imminent landing,
inkling trees and branchy shadow,
shade-to-be for sailors listening,
chins uplifted, ears as wide as
night with listening, hearing passing
birds: *oyeron pasar los pájaros*
all that mariner night of noises
mingling into avian passage
pinion-tacking over the caravels.

All the night, the whole night-roundness
global as earth, the rotund planet,
birds and ships were heard in passage,

birds by ships, and ships by fishes
marveling under cloven waters
where the *Pinta* spattered the fathom,
narrow the *Nina* startled the dolphin,
longer *Maria* with more of footage
freshened the seas with silver issue.
All that night they sailed the roundness,
heard that roundness birdlike passing
all the curving night above them,
while they sought awry an orient,
found false orient and trued it,
roaded error into finding,
found Cathay amid Antilles,
found a verity of roundness,
founded earth, its right conformance,
found their west and steered upon it,
sailed within its arc-ing wholeness,
heard it roundly and completely
swelling up their ears with passage:
listening men become enlarged with
truth, for they had held it total
filling them.
        Landing is logical
after ocean, is the passage
come to moment-haven, anchor
lowered after weeks of water
leaning westward, meaning eastward,
landing a navigator shoreward,
furrowing earthward through Atlantic
under night-clandestine plumage
pointing ships to candid harbor,
out of watches terse with passage
where all night they listened deeply
learning landing like an answer
waiting on their sea of question,

seizing image of America,
taking hemisphere, a moorage
early in the breaking morning.

What is shore if not a passage
firm conveyance to the interior,
farther trek to more of coastline,
into other surf and travel,
new Pacifics, nameless landfalls,
still equivocal for mapping?
What is westward if the world is
all around, within, without us,
over us and turning under us
beckoning ships and men in transit
as the birds that seethe the darkness
flash and beacon us with alary
brightness by their fringing passage
toward the dawn-watch of discovery?

How the flight of bird-fine music
floats its silken passage over us,
sweetens us with tone and tidings,
smartens us for terra firma
after journeys salt-encrusted,
wind-abraded, longing-weakened.
How the land is loosed from ocean:
Asia same and seeming counter,
Africa envisioned backwards,
paradoxes sighted proudly,
continents by morning kindled,
seas released beyond their boundaries,
further lands, and further fathoms,
upward, outward, reaching roundward
where cartographers go lightly
guessing contour and conclusion.

And we passengers in transience
from familiar in invention
in a latter-day connaissance
like Columbia explorers
latitudinal in orbits
keeping orderly their courses:
we who pass the night of coursing,
rafted through the nightfall crossing
realize our long intention
by the breaching light of morning.
And we mark our seas and spaces,
note our heralds, how in passage
they confirm the distant passage
closing in for our acquaintance,
bringing firmament beside us:
intimate and boldly slated
sequence of our nightsome vagrance
ending now in glim and portent
as of birds that once were passing
over men from Palos harbor
as of land beyond all ocean
all that night before America,
all the night they heard birds passing.

❧

This was the Age of Exploration. Under Prince Henry the Navigator,
Portugal pioneered sea routes along West Africa. Other nations
quickly took up the excitement of seeking new horizons. It remained for Spain, enlisting an Italian captain, Christopher Columbus, to find the greatest prize of all, a New World.

The concept of a round world was not so uniquely Columbian in
1492 as these verses imply, but Columbus was the first man really to
try to prove it at his own (and his crew's) risk. After an agonizingly
long voyage from the port of Palos in Spain, his seamen sick, weary,
and ripe for mutiny, the sound of birds flying overhead in the night

(109)

signalled a nearness of land. On October 12, his ships reached what seems to have been Watling Island in the Bahamas and the discovery of America, the opening of a whole continent and several centuries of further exploration of the globe was under way.

A.D. 1513

FLODDEN from MARMION

by Sir Walter Scott

But as they left the dark'ning heath,
More desperate grew the strife of death.
The English shafts in volleys hail'd,
In headlong charge their horse assail'd;
Front, flank, and rear, the squadrons sweep
To break the Scottish circle deep,
    That fought around their King.
But yet, though thick the shafts as snow,
Though charging knights like whirlwinds go,
Though bill-men ply the ghastly blow,
    Unbroken was the ring:
The stubborn spear-men still made good
Their dark impenetrable wood,
Each stepping where his comrade stood,
    The instant that he fell.
No thought was there of dastard flight;
Link'd in the serried phalanx tight,
Groom fought like noble, squire like knight,
As fearlessly and well;
Till utter darkness closed her wing
O'er their thin host and wounded King.
Then skilful Surrey's sage commands
Led back from strife his shatter'd bands;
    And from the charge they drew,
As mountain-waves, from wasted lands,
    Sweep back to ocean blue.
Then did their loss the foemen know;
Their King, their Lords, their mightiest low,
They melted from the field as snow,

When streams are swoln, and south winds blow,
    Dissolves in silent dew.
Tweed's echoes heard the ceaseless plash,
    While many a broken band,
Disorder'd, through her currents dash
    To gain the Scottish land;
To tower and town, to down and dale,
To tell red Flodden's dismal tale,
And raise the universal wail.
Tradition, legend, tune, and song,
Shall many an age that wail prolong:
Still from the sire the son shall hear
Of the stern strife, and carnage drear,
    Of Flodden's fatal field,
Where shiver'd was fair Scotland's spear,
    And broken was her shield!

❦

James IV of Scotland placed his bets on France and lost when Henry VIII's army defeated his forces. James IV lost his life and Scotland, although permitted a nominal king, became an English subsidiary. Henry VIII did not succeed, however, in his claim to France.

c. A.D. 1520

From *WHY COME YE NAT TO COURTE?*

by John Skelton

He is set so hye
In his hierarchy
Of frantycke frenesy
And folysshe fantasy,
That in the Chambre of Starres
All maters there he marres;
Clappyng his rod on the borde,
No man dare speke a worde,
For he hath all the sayenge,
Without any renayenge;
He rolleth in his recordes,
He sayth, "Howe saye ye, my lordes?
Is not my reason good?"
Good euyn, good Robin Hood!
Some say yes, and some
Syt styll as they were dom!
Thus thwartyng ouver thom,
He ruleth all the roste
With braggynge and with bost;
Borne vp on euery side
With pompe and with pryde,
With, trompe vp, alleluya!
For Dame Philargerya
Hath so his herte in holde,
He loueth nothyng but golde.

For all their noble blode
He plucks them by the hode,
And shakes them by the eare

(113)

And brynges them in suche feare;
He bayeth them like a bere,
Like an oxe or a bull:
Their wittes, he sayth, are dull;
He sayth they haue no brayne
Their astate to mayntayne;
And maketh them to bow theyr kne
Before his maieste.
Juges of the kynges lawes,
He countys them foles and dawes;
Sergyantes of the coyfe eke,
He sayth they are to seke
In pledgynge of theyr case
At the Commune Place,
Or at the Kynges Benche;
He wryngeth them suche a wrenche,
That all our lerned men
Dare not set theyr penne
To plete a trew tryall
Within Westmynster hall;
In the Chauncery where he syttes,
But suche as he admyttes
None so hardy to speke.
Whether he be knyght or squyre,
All men must folow his desyre.

*

The he is Cardinal Wolsey, favorite of Henry VIII (who inherited the powerful prelate from his father, Henry VII) and, at the time of Skelton's attack, probably the most powerful man in England. Skelton invented his own form of English verse, the short, crisp, stabbing line perfectly suited to this type of satirical comment. His English, in a transitional stage between Chaucer and Shakespeare, reads quite easily if you take it boldly according to sound and remember that v's and u's had not yet been sorted out. The Star Chamber was a special court where un-English Activities, as defined by Wolsey, could be punished without appeal. The Robin Hood phrase implies that politeness is enforced by duress. Dame Philargerya translates as Mistress Moneylove.

Eventually, Wolsey, after failing his attempt at being elected Pope in the 1520's, fell from royal grace when he fumbled Henry's plea for a papal annulment of the king's first marriage to Catherine of Aragon. Wolsey died before he could suffer the full fate of other ex-favorites.

A.D. 1536

DEFILED IS MY NAME

by Anne Boleyn

Defiléd is my name full sore,
Through cruel spite and false report,
That I may say for evermore:
Farewell, my joy, adieu, comfort.
Full wrongfully ye judge of me;
Unto my fame a mortal wound;
Say what ye list—it will not be,
Ye seek for that cannot be found:
Defiléd is my name.

❦

There were a few happy, triumphant months when Anne Boleyn, a saucy lady-in-waiting, succeeded her deposed mistress, Catherine of Aragon, as wife to Henry VIII and Queen of England. But the child she was carrying turned out not to be the longed-for male heir, only an unwanted princess christened Elizabeth. King Henry, his eye already roving, pinned a charge of adultery on his new queen and she was beheaded in 1536. In a society where the writing of verse was neither oddity nor disgrace, she found it natural to pour out her helpless defense in the lines above.

A.D. 1540

LITTLE JACK HORNER

Anonymous

Little Jack Horner
Sat in the corner,
Eating a Christmas pie;
He put in his thumb,
And pulled out a plum,
And said, What a good boy am I!

❧

Jack Horner was a minor sixteenth-century prelate, steward to the abbot of Glastonbury. At the time when Henry VIII was gobbling up church properties, the clever Jack managed to get hold of the deeds to the manor of Mells and deliver them to the king who paid him off well for the favor.

LATIMER AND RIDLEY

by *William Wordsworth*

How fast the Marian death-list is unrolled!
See Latimer and Ridley in the might
Of Faith stand coupled for a common flight!
One (like those prophets whom God sent of old)
Transfigured, from this kindling hath foretold
A torch of indistinguishable light;
The Other gains a confidence as bold;
And thus they foil their enemy's despite.
The penal instruments, the shows of crime,
Are glorified while this once-mitred pair
Of saintly Friends the "murtherer's chain partake,
Corded, and burning at the social stake:"
Earth never witnessed object more sublime
In constancy, in fellowship more fair!

❦

Edward VI, successor to Henry VIII at ten years of age, died when
only fifteen, leaving the throne to his cousin, Lady Jane Grey. But
Lady Jane lacked the power to hold it. Edward's half-sister Mary
took over royal power and had Lady Jane executed in 1553. In her
short reign (to 1558), Mary, a loyal daughter of her church, tried to
reintroduce Catholicism as the religion of England. Her effort failed
against a country grown used to greater tolerance, but in the effort
she carried out fierce reprisals against Protestant leaders. Ridley and
Latimer, both bishops of the Anglican church, were burned together
at the stake. It was Latimer who said: "Be of good comfort, Master
Ridley. We shall this day light such a candle by God's grace in
England, as (I trust) shall never be out out." Mary herself, disap-
pointed in love, religion, and politics, died in bed.

A.D. 1571

LEPANTO

by G. K. Chesterton

White founts falling in the Courts of the sun,
And the Soldan of Byzantium is smiling as they run;
There is laughter like the fountains in that face of all men feared,
It stirs the forest darkness, the darkness of his beard,
It curls the blood-red crescent, the crescent of his lips,
For the inmost sea of all the earth is shaken with his ships.
They have dared the white republics up the capes of Italy,
They have dashed the Adriatic round the Lion of the sea,
And the Pope has cast his arms abroad for agony and loss,
And called the kings of Christendom for swords about the Cross.
The cold Queen of England is looking in the glass;
The shadow of the Valois is yawning at the Mass;
From evening isles fantastical rings faint the Spanish gun,
And the Lord upon the Golden Horn is laughing in the sun.

Dim drums throbbing, in the hills half heard,
Where only on a nameless throne a crownless prince has stirred,
Where, risen from a doubtful seat and half attainted stall,
The last knight of Europe takes weapons from the wall,
The last and lingering troubadour to whom the bird has sung,
That once went singing southward when all the world was young.
In that enormous silence, tiny and unafraid,
Comes up along a winding road the noise of the Crusade.

Strong gongs groaning as the guns boom far,
Don John of Austria is going to the war,
Stiff flags straining in the night-blasts cold,
In the gloom black-purple, in the glint old-gold,
Torchlight crimson on the copper kettle-drums,

Then the tuckets, then the trumpets, then the cannon, and
    he comes.
Don John laughing in the brave beard curled,
Spurning of his stirrups like the thrones of all the world,
Holding his head up for a flag of all the free.
Love-light of Spain—hurrah!
Death-light of Africa!
Don John of Austria
Is riding to the sea.

Mahound is in his paradise above the evening star,
(*Don John of Austria is going to the war.*)
He moves a mighty turban on the timeless houri's knees,
His turban that is woven of the sunsets and the seas.
He shakes his peacock gardens as he rises from his ease,
And he strides among the tree-tops and is taller than the trees,
And his voice through all the garden is a thunder sent to bring
Black Azrael and Ariel and Ammon on the wing.
Giants and the Genii,
Multiplex of wing and eye,
Whose strong obedience broke the sky
When Solomon was king.

They rush in red and purple from the red clouds of the morn,
From temples where the yellow gods shut up their eyes in scorn;
They rise in green robes roaring from the green hells of the sea
Where fallen skies and evil hues and eyeless creatures be;
On them the sea-valves cluster and the gray sea-forests curl,
Splashed with a splendid sickness, the sickness of the pearl;
They swell in sapphire smoke out of the blue cracks of the
    ground,—
They gather and they wonder and give worship to Mahound.
And he saith, "Break up the mountains where the hermitfolk
    can hide,
And sift the red and silver sands lest bone of saint abide,

And chase the Giaours flying night and day, not giving rest,
For that which was our trouble comes again out of the west.
We have set the seal of Solomon on all things under sun,
Of knowledge and of sorrow and endurance of things done,
But a noise is in the mountains, in the mountains, and I know
The voice that shook our palaces—four hundred years ago:
It is he that saith not 'Kismet'; it is he that knows not Fate;
It is Richard, it is Raymond, it is Godfrey in the gate!
It is he whose loss is laughter when he counts the wager worth,
Put down your feet upon him, that our peace be on the earth."
For he heard drums groaning and he heard guns jar,
(*Don John of Austria is going to the war*).
Sudden and still—hurrah!
Bolt from Iberia!
Don John of Austria
Is gone by Alcalar.

St. Michael's on his Mountain in the sea-roads of the north
(*Don John of Austria is girt and going forth.*)
Where the gray seas glitter and the sharp tides shift,
And the sea-folk labor and the red sails lift.
He shakes his lance of iron and he clasps his wings of stone;
His noise is gone through Normandy; the noise is gone alone;
The North is full of tangled things and texts and aching eyes
And dead is all the innocence of anger and surprise,
And Christian killeth Christian in a narrow dusty room,
And Christian dreadeth Christ that hath a newer face of doom,
And Christian hateth Mary that God kissed in Galilee,
But Don John of Austria is riding to the sea.
Don John calling through the blast and the eclipse
Crying with the trumpet, with the trumpet of his lips,
Trumpet that sayeth ha!
   Domino Gloria!
Don John of Austria
Is shouting to the ships.

   (121)

King Philip's in his closet with the Fleece about his neck
(*Don John of Austria is armed upon the deck.*)
The walls are hung with velvet that is black and soft as sin,
And little dwarfs creep out of it and little dwarfs creep in.
He holds a crystal phial that has colors like the moon,
He touches, and it tingles, and he trembles very soon,
And his face is as a fungus of a leprous white and gray
Like plants in the high houses that are shuttered from the day,
And death is in the phial and the end of noble work,
But Don John of Austria has fired upon the Turk.
Don John's hunting, and his hounds have bayed—
Booms away past Italy the rumor of his raid.
Gun upon gun, ha! ha!
Gun upon gun, hurrah!
Don John of Austria
Has loosed the cannonade.

The Pope was in his chapel before day or battle broke
(*Don John of Austria is hidden in the smoke.*)
The hidden room in man's house where God sits all the year,
The secret window whence the world looks small and very dear.
He sees as in a mirror on the monstrous twilight sea
The crescent of his cruel ships whose name is mystery;
They fling great shadows foe-wards, making Cross and Castle
     dark,
They veil the plumèd lions on the galleys of St. Mark;
And above the ships are palaces of brown, black-bearded chiefs,
And below the ships are prisons, where with multitudinous
     griefs,
Christian captives sick and sunless, all a laboring race repines
Like a race in sunken cities, like a nation in the mines.
They are lost like slaves that swat, and in the skies of morning
     hung
The stairways of the tallest gods when tyranny was young.
They are countless, voiceless, hopeless as those fallen or fleeing on

Before the high Kings' horses in the granite of Babylon.
And many a one grows witless in his quiet room in hell
Where a yellow face looks inward through the lattice of his cell,
And he finds his God forgotten, and he seeks no more a sign—
(*But Don John of Austria has burst the battle-line!*)
Don John pounding from the slaughter-painted poop,
Purpling all the ocean like a bloody pirate's sloop,
Scarlet running over on the silvers and the golds,
Breaking of the hatches up and bursting of the holds,
Thronging of the thousands up that labor under sea,
White for bliss and blind for sun and stunned for liberty.
Vivat Hispania!
Domino Gloria!
Don John of Austria
Has set his people free!

Cervantes on his galley sets the sword back in the sheath
(*Don John of Austria rides homeward with a wreath.*)
And he sees across a weary land a straggling road in Spain,
Up which a lean and foolish knight for ever rides in vain,
And he smiles, but not as Sultans smile, and settles back the
       blade. . . .
(*But Don John of Austria rides home from the Crusade.*)

❧

*Marred though it is by blatant racism and special pleading, Lepanto
still has a stirring, thoughtless excitement to it. Chesterton, a tireless
journalist, novelist, poet, and Catholic apologist, rescued an all but
forgotten hero in his Austrian John and set him on a pedestal to live
beside Horatius and Paul Revere. The aftermath of the victory at
Lepanto was as dreary as the battle was thrilling: diplomatic deals
were concluded with the Turkish enemy, Venice gave up her principal
strongholds in the Mediterranean which remained largely in Turkish
control.*

A.D. 1584

SIR FRANCIS DRAKE

Anonymous

Sir Francis, Sir Francis, Sir Francis is come;
Sir Robert, and eke Sir William his son,
And eke the good Earl of Huntington
Marched gallantly on the road.

Then came the Lord Chamberlain with his white staff,
And all the people began to laugh;
And then the Queen began to speak,
"You're welcome home, Sir Francis Drake."

You gallants all o' the British blood,
Why don't you sail o' the ocean flood?
I protest you're not all worth a filbert
If once compared to Sir Humphrey Gilbert.

For he went away on a rainy day,
And to the new-found land found out his way,
With many a gallant fresh and green,
And he ne'er came home again. God bless the Queen.

❦

Queen Elizabeth and court notables made formal greeting to Sir
Francis Drake after his return from sailing around the world. Sir
Humphrey Gilbert, another famous Elizabethan navigator, was lost
searching for a northwest passage from Atlantic to Pacific.

MARY QUEEN OF SCOTS

by Robert Burns

Now nature hangs her mantle green
   On every blooming tree,
And spreads her sheets o' daisies white
   Out o'er the grassy lea:
Now Phoebus cheers the crystal streams,
   And glads the azure skies;
But nought can glad the weary wight
   That fast in durance lies.

Now lav'rocks wake the merry morn,
   Aloft on dewy wing;
The merle, in his noontide bower,
   Makes woodland echoes ring;
The mavis wild, wi' mony a note,
   Sings drowsy day to rest:
In love and freedom they rejoice,
   Wi' care nor thrall opprest.

Now blooms the lily by the bank,
   The primrose down the brae;
The hawthorne's budding in the glen,
   And milk-white is the slae;
The meanest hind in fair Scotland
   May rove their sweets amang;
But I, the queen of a' Scotland,
   Maun lie in prison strang!

I was the queen o' bonny France,
   Where happy I hae been;

Fu' lightly rase I in the morn,
  As blithe lay down at e'en:
And I'm the sovreign of Scotland,
  And mony a traitor there;
Yet here I lie in foreign bands,
  And never-ending care.

But as for thee, thou false woman!—
  My sister and my fae,
Grim Vengeance yet shall whet a sword
  That through thy soul shall gae!
The weeping blood in woman's breast
  Was never known to thee;
Nor the balm that draps on wounds of woe
  Frae woman's pittying ee.

My son! my son! may kinder stars
  Upon thy fortune shine!
And may those pleasures gild they reign,
  That ne'er wad blink on mine!
God keep thee frae they mother's faes,
  Or turn their hearts to thee:
And where thou meet'st thy mother's friend,
  Remember him for me!

Oh! soon to me may summer suns
  Nae mair light up the morn!
Nae mair to me the autumn winds
  Wave o'er the yellow corn!
And in the narrow house o' death
  Let winter round me rave;
And the next flowers that deck the spring
  Bloom on my peaceful grave!

✺

Mary Stuart, Queen of Scots, alive, would always represent a threat to Elizabeth I. So Mary Stuart lost her head in 1587, after twenty years' imprisonment.

A.D. 1588

DRAKE'S DRUM

by Sir Henry Newbolt

Drake he's in his hammock an' a thousand mile away,
    (Capten, art tha sleepin' there below?),
Slung atween the round shot in Nombre Dios Bay,
    An' dreamin' arl the time o' Plymouth Hoe.
Yarnder lumes the Island, yarnder lie the ships,
    Wi' sailor lads a-dancin' heel-an'-toe,
An' the shore-lights flashin', an' the night-tide dashin',
    He sees et arl so plainly as he saw et long ago.

Drake he was a Devon man, an' ruled the Devon seas,
    (Capten, art tha sleepin' there below?),
Rovin' tho' his death fell, he went wi' heart at ease,
    An' dreamin' arl the time o' Plymouth Hoe.
"Take my drum to England, hang et by the shore,
    Strike et when your powder's runnin' low;
If the Dons sight Devon, I'll quit the port o' Heaven,
    An' drum them up the Channel as we drumm'd them long
      ago."

Drake he's in his hammock till the great Armadas come,
    (Capten, art tha sleepin' there below?),
Slung atween the round shot, listenin' for the drum,
    An' dreamin' arl the time o' Plymouth Hoe.
Call him on the deep sea, call him up the Sound,
    Call him when ye sail to meet the foe;
Where the old trade's plyin' and the old flag flyin',
    They shall find him ware and wakin', as they found him long
      ago!

It takes some digging to get through Sir Henry Newbolt's sticky dialect, but a feeling for Drake does come through, for Drake, the rough, tough, capable sailor man, for the Drake who, with Howard and Hawkins, could lead a fleet of small English ships to defeat the Spanish Armada (over 125 ships, gunpower of 3,165 cannons) that sailed into the Channel to menace England and the Protestant Queen who wouldn't marry the King of Spain. What Drake and his fellow Devon men left, storms finished off along the coast of Ireland.

A.D. 1588

EPITAPH ON THE EARL OF LEICESTER

by Sir Walter Raleigh

Here lies the noble Warrior that never blunted sword;
Here lies the noble Courtier that never kept his word;
Here lies his Excellency that govern'd all the state;
Here lies the Earl of Leicester, that all the world did hate.

❧

Leicester was Robert Dudley, handsome courtier and a favorite of Queen Elizabeth. Raleigh, himself a rival for royal patronage, is over-harsh; Dudley had many faults, but hardly the total falseness Raleigh paints above.

A.D. 1590

IVRY

by Thomas Babington Macaulay

Now glory to the Lord of Hosts, from whom all glories are!
And glory to our Sovereign Liege, King Henry of Navarre!
Now let there be the merry sound of music and of dance,
Through thy corn-fields green, and sunny vines, oh pleasant land
    of France!
And thou, Rochelle, our own Rochelle, proud city of the waters,
Again let rapture light the eyes of all thy mourning daughters.
As thou wert constant in our ills, be joyous in our joy;
For cold, and stiff, and still are they who wrought thy walls
    annoy.
Hurrah! hurrah! a single field hath turned the chance of war.
Hurrah! hurrah! for Ivry, and Henry of Navarre.

Oh! how our hearts were beating, when, at the dawn of day,
We saw the army of the League drawn out in long array;
With all its priest-led citizens, and all its rebel peers,
And Appenzel's stout infantry, and Egmont's Flemish spears.
There rode the brood of false Lorraine, the curses of our land;
And dark Mayenne was in the midst, a truncheon in his hand:
And, as we looked on them, we thought of Seine's empurpled
    flood,
And good Coligni's hoary hair all dabbled with his blood;
And we cried unto the living God, who rules the fate of war,
To fight for His own holy name, and Henry of Navarre.

The King is come to marshal us, in all his armor dressed;
And he has bound a snow-white plume upon his gallant crest.
He looked upon his people, and a tear was in his eye;
He looked upon the traitors, and his glance was stern and high.

(131)

Right graciously he smiled on us, as rolled from wing to wing,
Down all our line, a deafening shout, "God save our Lord the
    King!"
"And if my standard-bearer fall, as fall full well he may,
For never saw I promise yet of such a bloody fray,
Press where ye see my white plume shine, amidst the ranks of
    war,
And be your oriflamme to-day the helmet of Navarre."

Hurrah! the foes are moving. Hark to the mingled din,
Of fife, and steed, and trump, and drum, and roaring culverin.
The fiery Duke is pricking fast across Saint André's plain,
With all the hireling chivalry of Guelders and Almayne.
Now by the lips of those ye love, fair gentlemen of France,
Charge for the golden lilies,—upon them with the lance!
A thousand spurs are striking deep, a thousand spears in rest,
A thousand knights are pressing close behind the snow-white
    crest;
And in they burst, and on they rushed, while, like a guiding star,
Amidst the thickest carnage blazed the helmet of Navarre.

Now, God be praised, the day is ours. Mayenne hath turned his
    rein.
D'Aumale hath cried for quarter; the Flemish count is slain.
Their ranks are breaking like thin clouds before a Biscay gale;
The field is heaped with bleeding steeds, and flags, and cloven
    mail.
And then we thought on vengeance, and, all along our van,
"Remember Saint Bartholomew!" was passed from man to man.
But out spake gentle Henry, "No Frenchman is my foe:
Down, down with every foreigner, but let your brethren go."
Oh! was there ever such a knight, in friendship or in war,
As our Sovereign Lord, King Henry, the soldier of Navarre?

Ho! maidens of Vienna; ho! matrons of Lucerne!
Weep, weep, and rend your hair for those who never shall return.
Ho! Philip, send, for charity, thy Mexican pistoles,
That Antwerp monks may sing a mass for thy poor spearmen's
  souls.
Ho! gallant nobles of the League, look that your arms be bright;
Ho! burghers of St. Genevieve, keep watch and ward tonight;
For our God hath crushed the tyrant, our God hath raised the
  slave,
And mocked the counsel of the wise, and the valor of the brave.
Then glory to His holy name, from whom all glories are;
And glory to our Sovereign Lord, King Henry of Navarre!

❦

*Ivry was the final key battle of the Religious Wars that tore up
Europe from 1562 as Catholic and Protestant alliances slaughtered
each other in the name of Faith. References in the fourth and in the
next to last stanza are to the Massacre of St. Bartholomew in Paris
in 1572 when the streets and the Seine ran red with the blood of
Huguenots (French Protestants): Henry IV himself, not yet king, had
to fake a conversion to avoid being included in the killing. He is
supposed, cynically or logically, to have remarked: "Paris is worth a
Mass." He turned back to Protestantism two years later and knit
together, by intrigue, alliances, and a few murders of his own, a
coalition strong enough to defeat the Catholic powers and secure him
on the throne he had succeeded to in 1589.*

THE REVENGE

by Alfred, Lord Tennyson

At Flores in the Azores Sir Richard Grenville lay,
And a pinnace, like a fluttered bird, came flying from far away;
"Spanish ships of war at sea! We have sighted fifty-three!"
Then sware Lord Thomas Howard: " 'Fore God, I am no coward;
But I cannot meet them here, for my ships are out of gear,
And the half my men are sick. I must fly, but follow quick.
We are six ships of the line; can we fight with fifty-three?"

Then spake Sir Richard Grenville: "I know you are no coward;
You fly them for a moment to fight with them again.
But I've ninety men and more that are lying sick ashore.
I should count myself the coward if I left them, my Lord
    Howard,
To these Inquisition dogs and the devildoms of Spain."

So Lord Howard passed away with five ships of war that day,
Till he melted like a cloud in the silent summer heaven;
But Sir Richard bore in hand all his sick men from the land
Very carefully and slow,
Men of Bideford in Devon,
And we laid them on the ballast down below:
For we brought them all aboard,
And they blessed him in their pain, that they were not left to
    Spain;
To the thumbscrew and the stake, for the glory of the Lord.

He had only a hundred seamen to work the ship and to fight,
And he sailed away from Flores till the Spaniard came in sight,
With his huge sea-castles heaving upon the weather bow.

"Shall we fight or shall we fly?
Good Sir Richard, tell us now,
For to fight is but to die!
There'll be little of us left by the time this sun be set."
And Sir Richard said again: "We be all good English men.
Let us bang these dogs of Seville, the children of the devil,
For I never turned my back upon Don or devil yet."

Sir Richard spoke and he laughed, and we roared a hurrah, and so
The little *Revenge* ran on sheer into the heart of the foe,
With her hundred fighters on deck, and her ninety sick below;
For half of their fleet to the right and half to the left were seen,
And the little *Revenge* ran on through the long sea-lane between.

Thousands of their soldiers looked down from their decks and
    laughed,
Thousands of their seamen made mock at the mad little craft
Running on and on, till delayed
By their mountain-like *San Philip*, that, of fifteen hundred tons,
And up-shadowing high above us with her yawning tiers of guns,
Took the breath from our sails, and we stayed.

And while now the great *San Philip* hung above us like a cloud
Whence the thunderbolt will fall
Long and loud,
Four galleons drew away
From the Spanish fleet that day,
And two upon the larboard and two upon the starboard lay,
And the battle-thunder broke from them all.

But anon the great *San Philip*, she bethought herself and went,
Having that within her womb that had left her ill content;
And the rest they came aboard us, and they fought us hand to
    hand,
For a dozen times they came with their pikes and musqueteers,

And a dozen times we shook 'em off as a dog that shakes his ears
When he leaps from the water to the land.

And the sun went down, and the stars came out far over the
    summer sea,
But never a moment ceased the fight of the one and the
    fifty-three.
Ship after ship, the whole night long, their high-built galleons
    came,
Ship after ship, the whole night long, with her battle-thunder
    and flame;
Ship after ship, the whole night long, drew back with her dead
    and her shame.
For some were sunk and many were shattered, and so could fight
    us no more—
God of battles, was ever a battle like this in the world before?

For he said "Fight on! fight on!"
Though his vessel was all but a wreck;
And it chanced that, when half of the short summer night was
    gone,
With a grisly wound to be dressed he had left the deck,
But a bullet struck him that was dressing it suddenly dead,
And himself he was wounded again in the side and the head,
And he said "Fight on! fight on!"

And the night went down, and the sun smiled out far over the
    summer sea,
And the Spanish fleet with broken sides lay round us all in a ring;
But they dared not touch us again, for they feared that we still
    could sting,
So they watched what the end would be.
And we had not fought them in vain,
But in perilous plight were we,
Seeing forty of our poor hundred were slain,

And half of the rest of us maimed for life
In the crash of the cannonades and the desperate strife.
And the sick men down in the hold were most of them stark and
  cold,
And the pikes were all broken or bent, and the powder was all of
  it spent;
And the masts and the rigging were lying over the side;
But Sir Richard cried out in his English pride:
"We have fought such a fight for a day and a night
As may never be fought again!
We have won great glory, my men!
And a day less or more
At sea or ashore,
We die—does it matter when?
Sink me the ship, Master Gunner—sink her, split her in twain!
Fall into the hands of God, not into the hands of Spain!"

And the gunner said, "Aye, aye," but the seamen made reply:
"We have children, we have wives,
And the Lord has spared our lives.
We will make the Spaniard promise, if we yield, to let us go;
We shall live to fight again and to strike another blow."
And the lion there lay dying, and they yielded to the foe.

And the stately Spanish men to their flagship bore him then,
Where they laid him by the mast, old Sir Richard caught at last,
And they praised him to his face with their courtly foreign grace;
But he rose upon their decks, and he cried:
"I have fought for Queen and Faith like a valiant man and true;
I have only done my duty as a man is bound to do.
With a joyful spirit I, Sir Richard Grenville, die!"
And he fell upon their decks, and he died.

And they stared at the dead that had been so valiant and true,
And had holden the power and glory of Spain so cheap

That he dared her with one little ship and his English few;
Was he devil or man? He was devil for aught they knew,
But they sank his body with honor down into the deep.
And they manned the *Revenge* with a swarthier alien crew,
And away she sailed with her loss and longed for her own;
When a wind from the lands they had ruined awoke from sleep,
And the water began to heave and the weather to moan,
And or ever that evening ended a great gale blew,
And a wave like the wave that is raised by an earthquake grew,
Till it smote on their hulls and their sails and their masts and
    their flags,
And the whole sea plunged and fell on the shot-scattered navy
    of Spain,
And the little *Revenge* herself went down by the island crags
To be lost evermore in the main.

❧

A more accurate, if less dramatic count puts the Spanish fleet at
fifteen ships, but these were still long odds and don't detract from
Sir Richard's heroism. Perhaps Tennyson needed fifty-three for the
rhythm. Reference in final line of stanza three is to the tortures of the
Spanish Inquisition.

c. A.D. 1600

IMPORTUNE ME NO MORE!

by Elizabeth I of England

When I was fair and young, and favor gracéd me,
Of many was I sought, their mistress for to be:
But I did scorn them all, and answered them therefore
    "Go, go, go, seek some otherwhere!
      Importune me no more!"

How many weeping eyes I made to pine with woe,
How many sighing hearts, I have no skill to show:
Yet I the prouder grew, and answered them therefore
    "Go, go, go, seek some otherwhere!
      Importune me no more!"

Then spake fair *Venus's* son, that proud, victorious Boy,
And said, "Fine Dame! Since that you be so coy:
I will so pluck your plumes, that you shall say no more,
    'Go, go, go, seek some otherwhere!
      Importune me no more.'"

When he had spoke these words, such change grew in my breast,
That neither night nor day since that, I could take any rest,
Then, lo! I did repent that I had said before,
    "Go, go, go, seek some otherwhere!
      Importune me no more!"

❦

The unwanted daughter of Anne Boleyn grew up to sit on the throne
of England in some of her nation's most exciting years. She had
courtiers a-plenty, but these lines, written well past the flush of youth,
mingle regret at her own aloofness and perhaps a realization of the

difference between those past swains who courted her for love and the others who continued to court her for power and privilege long after beauty had fled.

Venus's son *is*, of course, Cupid. Importune should be read to rhyme with fortune, accent on its second syllable.

A.D. 1600

SONG IN PLAGUE-TIME

by Thomas Nashe

Adieu, farewell earth's bliss,
This world uncertain is;
Fond are life's lustful joys,
Death proves them all but toys,
None from his darts can fly.
I am sick, I must die.
   Lord have mercy on us!

Rich men, trust not in wealth,
Gold cannot buy you health;
Physic himself must fade,
All things to end are made.
The plague full swift goes by;
I am sick, I must die.
   Lord have mercy on us!

Beauty is but a flower
Which wrinkles will devour:
Brightness falls from the air,
Queens have died young and fair,
Dust hath closed Helen's eye.
I am sick, I must die.
   Lord have mercy on us!

Strength stoops unto the grave,
Worms feed on Hector brave,
Swords may not fight with fate.
Earth still holds ope her gate;
Come! come! the bells do cry.

I am sick, I must die.
　Lord have mercy on us!

Wit with his wantonness
Tasteth death's bitterness;
Hell's executioner
Hath no ears for to hear
What vain art can reply.
I am sick, I must die.
　Lord have mercy on us!

Haste, therefore, each degree,
To welcome destiny.
Heaven is our heritage,
Earth but a player's stage;
Mount we unto the sky.
I am sick, I must die.
　Lord have mercy on us!

THE LION AND THE UNICORN

Anonymous

The Lion and the Unicorn
  Were fighting for the Crown.
The Lion beat the Unicorn
  All round the town.

Some gave them white bread,
  Some gave them brown,
Some gave them plum cake,
  And drummed them out of town.

❧

Lion and Unicorn were heraldic figures on the Coats of Arms of England and Scotland, and the nursery rhyme seems to date from the accession of James VI of Scotland to the English throne as James I of England. Confusions in heraldry were settled by including both Unicorn and Lion in the new royal standard.

A.D. 1605

GUY FAWKES DAY

Anonymous

Please to remember
The Fifth of November,
Gunpowder treason and plot;
I see no reason
Why gunpowder treason
Should ever be forgot.

❧

James I tried too hard to balance the pressures in his kingdom between Catholic and Protestant and, in so doing, offended both sides. An edict banishing priests in 1604 inspired Robert Catesby and other conspirators to plan blowing up the houses of Parliament with barrels of gunpowder hidden in the cellars. Guy Fawkes, weakest of the gang, was caught and revealed the whole plot. His name, ever since, has been a byword for treachery, as much for his betrayal as for the treasonous plan itself.

A.D. 1645

THE BATTLE OF NASEBY

by Obadiah Bind-their-kings-in-chains-and-their-nobles-
with-links-of-iron, Serjeant in Ireton's Regiment

by Thomas Babington Macaulay

Oh! wherefore come ye forth, in triumph from the North
  With your hands, and your feet, and your raiment all red!
And wherefore doth your rout send forth a joyous shout?
  And whence be the grapes of the wine-press which ye tread?

Oh, evil was the root, and bitter was the fruit,
  And crimson was the juice of the vintage that we trod;
For we tramped upon the throng of the haughty and the strong,
  Who sate in the high places and slew the saints of God.

It was about the noon of a glorious day of June
  That we saw their banners dance and their cuirasses shine,
And the Man of Blood was there, with his long essencèd hair,
  And Astley, and Sir Marmaduke, and Rupert of the Rhine.

Like a servant of the Lord, with his Bible and his sword,
  The General rode along us to form us for the fight,
When a murmuring sound broke out, and swell'd into a shout,
  Among the godless horsemen upon the tyrant's right.

And hark! like the roar of the billows on the shore,
  The cry of battle rises along their charging line!
For God! for the Cause! for the Church! for the Laws!
  For Charles King of England, and Rupert of the Rhine!

The furious German comes, with his clarions and his drums,
  His bravoes of Alsatia and pages of Whitehall;

They are bursting on our flanks. Grasp your pikes:—close your
     ranks:—
   For Rupert never comes but to conquer or to fall.

They are here:—they rush on.—We are broken:—we are gone:—
   Our left is borne before them like the stubble on the blast.
O Lord put forth thy might! O Lord defend the right!
   Stand back to back in God's name, and fight it to the last.

Stout Skippon hath a wound:—the centre hath given ground:—
   Hark! hark!—What means the trampling of horsemen on our
     rear?
Whose banner do I see, boys? 'Tis he, thank God, 'tis he, boys.
   Bear up another minute. Brave Oliver is here.

Their heads all stooping low, their points all in a row,
   Like a whirlwind on the trees, like a deluge on the dykes,
Our cuirassers have burst on the ranks of the Accurst,
   And at a shock have scattered the forest of his pikes.

Fast, fast, the gallants ride, in some safe nook to hide
   Their coward heads, predestinèd to rot on Temble-Bar,
And he—he turns, he flies,—shame on those cruel eyes
   That bore to look on torture, and dare not look on war.

Ho! comrades, scour the plain: and, ere ye strip the slain,
   First give another stab to make your quest secure,
Then shake from sleeves and pockets their broad-pieces and
     lockets,
   The tokens of the wanton, the plunder of the poor.

Fools, your doublets shone with gold, and your hearts were gay
     and bold,
   When you kissed your lily hands to your lemans to-day;

(146)

And tomorrow shall the fox, from her chambers in the rocks,
  Lead forth her tawny cubs to howl above the prey.

Where be your tongues that late mocked at heaven and hell and
    fate,
  And the fingers that once were so busy with your blades,
Your perfumed satin clothes, your catches and your oaths,
  Your stage-plays and your sonnets, your diamonds and your
    spades?

Down, down, for ever down with the mitre and the crown,
  With the Belial of the court, and the Mammon of the Pope;
There is woe in Oxford Halls; there is wail in Durham's Stalls:
  The Jesuit smites his bosom: the Bishop rends his cope.

And She of the seven hills shall mourn her children's ills,
  And tremble when she thinks on the edge of England's sword;
And the Kings of earth in fear, shall shudder when they hear
  What the hand of God hath wrought for the Houses and the
    Word.

❧

*Not so simply stirring as Horatius, but here Macaulay has done a
more masterly job of getting inside the skin of his angry, God-
drunken, righteously victorious Puritan narrator. And, psychologically,
he gives more than an inkling of the envy and bitterness that can
infect even the best of causes. Rupert of the Rhine (the furious German) was a cousin of King Charles I and, if not the best, the most
flamboyant of Cavalier generals. She of the seven hills is the Roman
Catholic Church and the Houses, of course, are that Parliament
Catesby failed to blow up. After Naseby, there was no further hope
for the King's cause. Cromwell (the Brave Oliver of stanza eight),
after factional struggles among the puritans themselves, became Lord
Protector of England from 1653 to 1658 when he died and was
succeeded by his son, Richard. Charles I had been beheaded in 1649.*

(147)

A.D. 1649

LAMENT FOR THE DEATH OF
EOGHAN RUADH O'NEILL

by Thomas Davis

Time: 10 November, 1649. Scene: Ormond's Camp, County
Waterford. Speakers: a Veteran of Eoghan O'Neill's clan,
and one of the horsemen just arrived with news of his death.
(Eoghan Ruadh, translates as Red-Haired Owen.)

"Did they dare, did they dare, to slay Eoghan Ruadh O'Neill?"
"Yes, they slew with poison him they feared to meet with steel."
"May God wither up their hearts! May their blood cease to flow!
May they walk in living death, who poisoned Eoghan Ruadh!

"Though it break my heart to hear, say again the bitter words."
"From Derry, against Cromwell, he marched to measure swords;
But the weapon of the Saxon met him on his way,
And he died at Cloch Uachtar, upon Saint Leonard's Day."

Wail, wail ye for the Mighty One! Wail, wail ye for the Dead;
Quench the hearth, and hold the breath—with ashes strew the
  head.
How tenderly we loved him! How deeply we deplore!
Holy Saviour! but to think we shall never see him more!

"Sagest in the council was he, kindest in the Hall:
Sure we never won a battle—'twas Eoghan won them all.
Had he lived—had he lived—our dear country had been free;
But he's dead, but he's dead, and 'tis slaves we'll ever be.

"O'Farrell and Clanricarde, Preston and Red Hugh,
Audley and Mac Mahon—ye are valient, wise, and true;

But—what, what are ye all to our darling who is gone?
The Rudder of our ship was he, our Castle's corner-stone!

"Wail him, wail him through the Island! Weep, weep for our
    pride!
Would that on the battle-field our gallant chief had died!
Weep the victor of Benurb—weep him, young man and old;
Weep for him, ye women—your Beautiful lies cold!

"We thought you would not die—we were sure you would not go,
And leave us in our utmost need to Cromwell's cruel blow—
Sheep without a shepherd, when the snow shuts out the sky—
Oh! why did you leave us, Eoghan? Why did you die?

"Soft as woman's was your voice, O'Neill! bright was your eye,
Oh! why did you leave us, Eoghan? Why did you die?
Your troubles are all over, you're at rest with God on high;
But we're slaves, and we're orphans, Eoghan!—why did you die?"

❧

The Irish, many of them still loyal to the defeated and executed
Charles I, were a stubborn thorn in Cromwell's side. Cromwell put
down their resistance with brutal force and massacres at Wexford and
Drogheda. His name, even today in Ireland, is about as revered as
that of Hitler in Czechoslovakia.

A.D. 1663

THE PRESBYTERIAN from HUDIBRAS

by Samuel Butler

For his Religion it was fit
To match his Learning and his Wit:
'Twas Presbyterian true blew;
For he was of that stubborn Crew
Of errant Saints, whom all men grant
To be the true Church Militant;
Such as do build their Faith upon
The holy Text of Pike and Gun;
Decide all Contraversies by
Infallible Artillery;
And prove their Doctrine Orthodox
By Apostolick Blows and Knocks;
Call Fire and Sword and Desolation,
A godly-thorough-Reformation,
Which always must be carried on,
And still be doing, never done;
As if Religion were intended
For nothing else but to be mended:
A Sect whose chief Devotion lies
In odd perverse Antipathies;
In falling out with that or this
And finding somewhat still amiss:
More peevish, cross, and splenetick,
Than Dog distract, or Monky sick,
That with more care keep Holy-day
The wrong than others the right way;
Compound for Sins they are inclin'd to
By damning those they have no mind to.
Still so perverse and opposite

As if they worshipp'd God for spight,
The self-same thing they will abhor
One way and long another for.
Free-will they one way disavow,
Another nothing else allow:
All piety consists therein
In them, in other Men all Sin:
Rather than fail, they will defie
That which they love most tenderly,
Quarrel with minc'd Pies, and disparage
Their best and dearest friend, Plum-porridge;
Fat Pig and Goose it self oppose,
And blaspheme Custard through the Nose.
Th'Apostles of this fierce Religion,
Like Mahomet's were Ass and Widgeon,
To whom our Knight, by fast instinct
Of Wit and Temper was so linkt,
As if Hipocrisie and Non-sence
Had got th'Avouson of his Conscience.

❦

Richard Cromwell lacked his father's abilities, especially that of
holding army, parliament, and religious leaders together. He was
forced to resign in 1658 and in 1660 General Monk brought back
Charles II from his exile in France. The years of this Restoration were
busy and merry. Charles II was not over-vindictive toward his recent
enemies, but the poet, Samuel Butler, assured himself of royal favor
(and a pension from the royal purse) by his barbed satire on the
Presbyterians, farthest-out of the large puritan sects.

(151)

A.D. 1655

ON THE MASSACRE IN PIEDMONT

by John Milton

Avenge, O Lord, thy slaughtered saints, whose bones
  Lie scattered on the Alpine mountains cold;
  Even them who kept thy truth so pure of old,
  When all our fathers worshiped stocks and stones,
Forget not. In thy book record their groans
  Who were thy sheep, and in their ancient fold
  Slain by the bloody Piedmontese, that rolled
  Mother with infant down the rocks. Their moans
The vales redoubled to the hills, and they
  To heaven. Their martyred blood and ashes sow
  O'er all the Italian fields where still doth sway
The triple tyrant; that from these may grow
  A hundred-fold, who having learnt thy way
  Early may fly the Babylonian woe.

❦

Butler could put together his barbed rhymes against dour Presby-
terians, but this was not typical of all English feeling. When Charles
Emmanuel II of Savoy countenanced the slaughter of scores of
Waldenses (Protestant followers of Peter Waldo, a thirteenth-century
religious reformer), John Milton wrote a sonnet which has endured
beyond most memories either of Charles or of Peter Waldo.

A.D. 1665

PLAGUE CHARM

Anonymous

Ring-a-ring o' roses,
A pocket full of posies.
   A-tishoo! A-tishoo!
We all fall down.

The version I first learned as a child was slightly changed (perhaps by crossing the Atlantic) to:

Ring around the rosie,
Pocket full of posies.
   Ashes! Ashes!
All fall down.

❦

There must be several other versions, but all stem from the London of the Great Plague when the roses and the pocket full of posies referred to scented sachets carried to mask the stench of death and disease and, hopefully, to ward off infection. The third line imitates the foreboding sound of a sneeze, a first sign of illness, and all fall down . . . dead.

LONDON MOURNING IN ASHES

Or, Lamentable Narrative lively expressing the Ruine of that
Royal City by fire which began in Pudding-lane on September
the second, 1666, at one of the clock in the morning being
Sunday, and continuing until Thursday night following, being
the sixth day, with the great care the King, and the Duke of
York took in their own persons, day and night to quench it.

Anonymous Ballad

The Tune, *In sad and ashy weeds.*

Of Fire, Fire, Fire I sing,
   that have more cause to cry,
In the Great Chamber of the King
   (a City mounted High);
Old London that,
Hath stood in State,
   above six hundred years,
In six days space,
Woe and alas!
   is burn'd and drown'd in tears.

The second of *September* in
   the middle time of night,
In *Pudding-lane* it did begin,
   to burn and blaze out right;
Where all that gaz'd,
Were so amaz'd,
   at such a furious flame,
They knew not how,

Or what to do
    that might expel the same.

It swallow'd *Fishstreet hil*, and straight
    it lick'd up *Lombard-street*,
Down *Canon-street* in blazing State
    it flew with flaming feet;
Down to the *Thames*
    Whose shrinking streams,
        began to ebb away;
    As thinking that
    The power of Fate
        had brought the latter day.

*   *   *   *   *   *   *

The Crackling flames do fume and roar,
    as billows do retyre,
The City (though upon the shoar)
    doth seem a sea of fire;
Where Steeple Spires
Shew in the Fires,
    like Vessels sinking down.
The open fields,
More safety yields,
    and thither fly the Town.

*   *   *   *   *   *   *

From *Sunday* morn, till *Thursday* at night,
    it roared about the Town,
There was no way to quell its might
    but to pull Houses down;
And so they did,
As they were bid
    By *Charles*, His Great Command;
The Duke of *York*,

(155)

Some say did work,
  with Bucket in his hand.

*   *   *   *   *   *   *

Although the Fire be fully quench'd
  yet if our sins remain,
And that in them we still are drench'd,
  the Fire will rage again;
Or what is worse,
A heavier Curse,
  in Famine will appear;
Where shall we tread,
When want of Bread,
  and Hunger draweth near.

If this do not reform our lives,
  A worse thing will succeed,
Our kindred, children, and our wives,
  will dye for want of Bread;
When Famine comes,
'Tis not our Drums,
  Our ships or Horse or Foot,
That can defend,
But if we mend,
  we never shall come to't.

A.D. 1674

CHARLES THE SECOND
from THE HISTORY OF THE INSIPIDS

by John Wilmot, Earl of Rochester

Chast, pious, prudent, Charles the Second
The Miracle of thy Restauration,
May like to that of Quails be reckon'd
Rain'd on the Israelitick Nation;
The wisht-for Blessing from Heav'n sent,
Became their Curse and Punishment.

The Vertues in thee, Charles inherent,
Although thy countenance be an odd piece,
Proves thee as true a Gods Viceregent
As e're was Harry with the Codpiece:
For Chastity and pious Deeds,
His Grandsire Harry, Charles exceeds.

Never was such a Faith's Defender,
He, like a politick Prince, and pious,
Gives liberty to Conscience tender,
And doth to no Religion tie us.
Jews, Christians, Turks, Papists, he'll please us,
With Moses, Mohomet, or Jesus.

In all Affairs of Church or State,
He very zealous is, and able,
Devout at Prayers, and sits up late
At the Cabal and Council Table.
His very Dog at Council Board,
Sits grave and wise, as any Lord.

(157)

Let Charles his Policy no Man flout,
The wisest Kings have all some Folly
Nor let his Piety any doubt;
Charles like a Sovreign wise and holy,
Makes young Men Judges of the Bench,
And Bishops some that love a Wench.

His Father's Foes he doth reward,
Preserving those that cut off's Head:
Old Cavaliers the Crown's best Guard,
He lets them starve for want of Bread.
Never was any King endow'd
With so much Grace and Gratitude.

Blood, that wears Treason in his Face,
Villain compleat in Parson's Gown,
How much is he at Court in Grace
For stealing Ormond, and the Crown?
Since Loyalty do's no Man good,
Let's steal the King and out-do Blood.

A Parliament of Knaves and Sots
Members by name, you must not mention,
He keeps in Pay, and buys their Votes,
Here with a Place, there with a Pension
When to give Mony he can't cologue 'um,
He doth with Scorn prorogue, prorogue 'um.

But they long since by too much giving,
Undid, betray'd, and sold the Nation;
Making their Memberships a Living,
Better than e're was Sequestration.
God give thee, Charles, a Resolution
To damn the Knaves by a Dissolution.

Rochester was soldier, sailor, rake, poet, dramatist, and even quack doctor, but perhaps his greatest talent was continuing to be a court favorite of Charles II despite verses like our example.

The two ancestral Harrys in stanza two are, respectively, Henry VIII of England and Henry IV of France. Blood in stanza seven is the celebrated Colonel Thomas Blood who tried, both attempts unsuccessful, to kidnap the Duke of Ormonde and to steal the Crown Jewels from the Tower of London; instead of punishing him, Charles II put him on payroll as a secret agent.

A.D. 1677

LUCY LOCKET

Anonymous

Lucy Locket lost her pocket,
Kitty Fisher found it;
Not a penny was there in it,
Only ribbon round it.

❧

Both Lucy Locket and Kitty Fisher were real people, well-known courtesans in the merry days of Charles II. Nobody seems to know what incident of scandal or professional rivalry led to their inclusion in this nonsense-nursery rhyme.

A.D. 1688

THE SONG OF THE WESTERN MEN

by Robert Hawker

A good sword and a trusty hand!
  A merry heart and true!
King James's men shall understand
  What Cornish lads can do.

And have they fixed the where and when?
  And shall Trelawney die?
Here's twenty thousand Cornish men
  Will know the reason why!

Out spake their captain brave and bold,
  A merry wight was he:
"If London Tower were Michael's hold,
  We'll set Trelawney free!

"We'll cross the Tamer, land to land,
  The Severn is no stay,
With 'one and all,' and hand in hand,
  And who shall bid us nay?

"And when we come to London Wall,
  A pleasant sight to view,
Come forth! come forth, ye cowards all,
  Here's men as good as you!

"Trelawney he's in keep and hold.
  Trelawney he may die;
But here's twenty thousand Cornish bold,
  Will know the reason why!"

(161)

Trelawney of Bristol was one of seven bishops locked up by James II for refusing to read the Declaration of Indulgence, a return of rights to Roman Catholics. Along with his colleagues he was acquitted by a jury, and Catholics in England had to do without full civil rights for another century and a half. James II was already deep in trouble and on November 5 of the same year his nephew, William of Orange, landed at Torbay to become William III of England. James kept his head, but died in exile in France.

A.D. 1689

THE BATTLE OF KILLIEKRANKIE

by W. E. Aytoun

Soon we heard a challenge-trumpet
   Sounding in the pass below,
And the distant tramp of horses,
   And the voices of the foe:
Down we crouched amid the bracken,
   Till the Lowland ranks drew near,
Panting like the hounds in summer,
   When they scent the stately deer.
From the dark defile emerging,
   Next we saw the squadrons come,
Leslie's foot and Leven's troopers
   Marching to the tuck of drum;
Through the scattered wood of birches,
   O'er the broken ground and heath,
Wound the long battalion slowly,
   Till they gained the plain beneath;
Then we bounded from our covert.—
   Judge how looked the Saxons then,
When they saw the rugged mountain
   Start to life with armèd men!

Like a tempest down the ridges
   Swept the hurricane of steel,
Rose the slogan of Macdonald—
   Flashed the broadsword of Lochiel!
Vainly sped the withering volley
   'Mongst the foremost of our band—
On we poured until we met them,
   Foot to foot, and hand to hand.

(163)

Horse and man went down like driftwood
  When the floods are black at Yule,
And their carcasses are whirling
  In the Garry's deepest pool.
Horse and man went down before us—
  Living foe there tarried none
On the field at Killiekrankie,
  When that stubborn fight was done!

And the evening star was shining
  On Schehallion's distant head,
When we wiped our bloody broadswords,
  And returned to count the dead.
There we found him gashed and gory,
  Stretched upon the cumbered plain,
As he told us where to seek him,
  In the thickest of the slain.
And a smile was on his visage,
  For within his dying ear
Pealed the joyful note of triumph,
  And the clansman's clamorous cheer:
So, amidst the battle's thunder,
  Shot, and steel, and scorching flame,
In the glory of his manhood
  Passed the spirit of the Graeme!

❧

The exiled James II made abortive efforts to regain his lost kingdom. John Graham (or Graeme), Viscount Claverhouse, lovingly nick-named "Bonnie Dundee," led the most spectacular and routed an English force at Killiekrankie, but lost his own life at the moment of victory. After his death, the revolt fell apart.

A.D. 1704

THE BATTLE OF BLENHEIM

by Robert Southey

It was a summer evening,
　Old Kaspar's work was done,
And he before his cottage door
　Was sitting in the sun;
And by him sported on the green
His little grandchild Wilhelmine.

She saw her brother Peterkin
　Roll something large and round,
Which he beside the rivulet
　In playing there had found:
He came to ask what he had found,
That was so large, and smooth, and round.

Old Kaspar took it from the boy,
　Who stood expectant by;
And then the old man shook his head,
　And with a natural sigh,
" 'Tis some poor fellow's skull," said he,
"Who fell in the great victory!

"I find them in the garden,
　For there's many here about;
And often when I go to plough,
　The ploughshare turns them out;
For many thousand men," said he,
"Were slain in that great victory!"

(165)

"Now tell us what 'twas all about,"
  Young Peterkin he cries;
And little Wilhelmine looks up
  With wonder-waiting eyes;
"Now tell us all about the war,
And what they fought each other for."

"It was the English," Kaspar cried,
  "Who put the French to rout;
But what they fought each other for
  I could not well make out;
But everybody said," quoth he,
"That 'twas a famous victory!

"My father lived at Blenheim then,
  Yon little stream hard by;
They burned his dwelling to the ground
  And he was forced to fly;
So with his wife and child he fled,
Nor had he where to rest his head.

"With fire and sword the country round
  Was wasted far and wide:
And many a childing mother then,
  And new-born baby died;
But things like that, you know, must be
At every famous victory.

"They say it was a shocking sight
  After the field was won;
For many thousand bodies here
  Lay rotting in the sun;
But things like that, you know, must be
After a famous victory.

(166)

"Great praise the Duke of Marlboro' won,
  And our good Prince Eugene."
"Why, 'twas a very wicked thing!"
  Said little Wilhelmine.
"Nay, nay, my little girl," quoth he;
"It was a famous victory!

"And everybody praised the Duke
  Who such a fight did win."
"But what good came of it at last?"
  Quoth little Peterkin.
"Why that I cannot tell," said he;
"But 'twas a famous victory!"

Blenheim was a key battle in the War of the Spanish Succession (which nonetheless dragged on for ten more years) and a major stepping stone in the career of John Churchill, Duke of Marlborough, an ancestor of our nearer English hero, Sir Winston Churchill. It was, as old Kaspar said, a famous victory and it settled very little.

A.D. 1709

From ALEXANDER SELKIRK

by William Cowper

I am monarch of all I survey,
    My right there is none to dispute;
From the centre all round to the sea,
    I am lord of the fowl and the brute.
O Solitude! where are thy charms
    That sages have seen in thy face?
Better dwell in the midst of alarms
    Than reign in this horrible place.

I am out of humanity's reach,
    I must finish my journey alone,
Never hear the sweet music of speech,
    I start at the sound of my own.
The beasts that roam over the plain,
    My form with indifference see;
They are so unacquainted with man,
    Their tameness is shocking to me.

Alexander Selkirk, a seaman in the privateering mission of Captain
William Dampier, was put ashore after a quarrel with his captain on
the uninhabited island of Juan Fernandez in 1704. He stuck it out for
five years until a passing ship rescued him in 1709. His experiences
were used by Defoe as the basis for Robinson Crusoe and the genesis
for a thousand desert-island jokes.

A.D. 1709

From *MAZEPPA*

by George Gordon, Lord Byron

Away, away, my steed and I,
Upon the pinions of the wind,
All human dwellings left behind;
We sped like meteors through the sky,
When with its crackling sound the night
Is chequer'd with the northern light:
Town—village—none were on our track,
But a wild plain of far extent,
And bounded by a forest black;
And, save the scarce-seen battlement
On distant heights of some strong hold,
Against the Tartars built of old,
No trace of man. The year before
A Turkish army had marched o'er;
And where the Spahi's hoof hath trod,
The verdure flies the bloody sod:
The sky was dull, and dim, and gray,
And a low breeze crept moaning by—
I could have answered with a sigh—
But fast we fled, away, away.
And I could neither sigh nor pray;
And my cold sweat-drops fell like rain
Upon the courser's bristling mane;
But, snorting still with rage and fear,
He flew upon his far career:
At times I almost thought, indeed,
He must have slackened in his speed;
But no—my bound and slender frame
Was nothing to his angry might,

(169)

And merely like a spur became:
Each motion which I made to free
My swoln limbs from their agony
Increased his fury and affright:
I tried my voice,—'twas faint and low,
But yet he swerved as from a blow;
And, starting to each accent, sprang
As from a sudden trumpet's clang:
Meantime my cords were wet with gore,
Which, oozing through my limbs, ran o'er;
And in my tongue the thirst became
A something fierier far than flame.

Mazeppa was a Cossack chief who allied himself with Charles XII
of Sweden in his campaign against Peter the Great of Russia. It was
not a wise choice. Peter defeated the Swedes at Poltova and Mazeppa
escaped with Charles to Turkey. Byron's verses record an earlier Cossack adventure when Mazeppa was tied to a wild horse as punishment
for an affair with another man's wife.

CHARLES XII from THE VANITY OF HUMAN WISHES

by Samuel Johnson

On what Foundation stands the warrior's pride?
How just his hopes let *Swedish Charles* decide;
A frame of adamant, a soul of fire,
No dangers fright him, and no labors tire;
O'er love, o'er fear, extends his wide domain,
Unconquer'd lord of pleasure and of pain;
No Joys to him pacific scepters yield,
War sounds the trump, he rushes to the field;
Behold surrounding kings their pow'r combine,
And one capitulate, and one resign;
Peace courts his hand, but spreads her charms in vain;
"Think nothing gain'd," he cries, "till nought remain,
"On *Moscow's* walls till *Gothic* standards fly,
"And all be mine beneath the polar sky."
The march begins in military state,
And nations on his eye suspended wait:
Stern Famine guards the solitary coast,
And Winter barricades the Realms of Frost;
He comes, not want and cold his course delay;—
Hide, blushing Glory, hide *Pultowa's* day:
The vanquish'd hero leaves his broken bands,
And shows his miseries in distant lands;
Condemn'd a needy supplicant to wait,
While ladies interpose, and slaves debate.
But did not Chance at length her error mend?
Did not subverted empire mark his end?
Did rival monarchs give the fatal wound?
Or hostile millions press him to the ground?

His fall was destin'd to a barren strand,
A petty fortress, and a dubious hand;
He left the name, at which the world grew pale,
To point a moral, or adorn a tale.

A.D. 1722

A SATYRICAL ELEGY

On the Death of a Late Famous General

by Jonathan Swift

His Grace! impossible! what dead!
Of old age, too, and in his bed!
And could that mighty warrior fall?
And so inglorious, after all!
Well, since he's gone, no matter how,
The last loud trump must wake him now:
And, trust me, as the noise grows stronger,
He'd wish to sleep a little longer.
And could he be indeed so old
As by the news-papers we're told?
Threescore, I think, is pretty high;
'Twas time in conscience he should die,
This world he cumber'd long enough:
He burnt his candle to the snuff;
And that's the reason, some folks think,
He left behind *so great a stink.*
Behold his funeral appears,
Nor widow's sighs, nor orphan's tears,
Wont at such times each heart to pierce,
Attend the progress of his hearse.
But what of that, his friends may say,
He had those honors in his day.
True to his profit and his pride,
He made them weep before he dy'd.

Come hither, all ye empty things,
Ye bubbles rais'd by breath of Kings;
Who float upon the tide of state,

Come hither, and behold your fate.
Let pride be taught by this rebuke,
How very mean a thing's a Duke;
From all his ill-got honors flung,
Turn'd to that dirt from whence he sprung.

❦

The General was John Churchill, Duke of Marlborough, victor at
the "famous victory" Southey celebrates in The Battle of Blenheim
(q.v.). He seems to have been a quite unpleasant old gentleman with
a sensationally vicious politicking wife, but still not quite the monster
that Swift, a political enemy, presents. For a total of contrast in
elegies, see Disraeli's Wellington.

A.D. 1740

HIGH GERMANY

Anonymous Ballad

He: O Polly love, O Polly, the route has now begun,
And we must be a-marching at the beating of the drum:
Go dress yourself in all your best and come along with me,
I'll take you to the cruel wars in High Germany.

She: Oh, cursed are the cruel wars that ever they should rise,
And out of merry England press many a lad likewise;
They pressed my Harry from me as all my brothers three,
And sent them to the cruel wars in High Germany.

❧

The cruel wars were The War of the Austrian Succession, a dynastic
conflict over a central European throne that engulfed most of the
European-influenced world from 1740 to 1748, including the American colonies of England, France, and Spain. Settled by the Treaty of
Aix-La-Chapelle in October, 1748. Harry was torn from his Polly by
English army press-gangs, the impressment of soldiers being an early,
rough-and-ready form of draft. This was the last great war in which
an (approximately) English monarch, George II, led his own troops,
at the battle of Dettingen in 1743.

A.D. 1769

A ST. HELENA LULLABY

by *Rudyard Kipling*

"How far is St. Helena from a little child at play?"
What makes you want to wander there with all the world
  between?
Oh, Mother, call your son again or else he'll run away.
(*No one thinks of winter when the grass is green!*)

"How far is St. Helena from a fight in a Paris street?"
I haven't time to answer now—the men are falling fast.
The guns begin to thunder, and the drums begin to beat.
(*If you take the first step, you will take the last!*)

"How far is St. Helena from the field of Austerlitz?"
You couldn't hear me if I told you—so loud the cannon roar.
But not so far for people who are living by their wits.
(*"Gay go up" means "Gay go down" the wide world o'er!*)

"How far is St. Helena from an Emperor of France?"
I cannot see—I cannot tell—the crowns they dazzle so.
The Kings sit down to dinner, and the Queens stand up to dance.
(*After open weather you may look for snow!*)

"How far is St. Helena from the Capes of Trafalgar?"
A longish way—a longish way—with ten year more to run.
It's South across the water underneath a falling star.
(*What you cannot finish you must leave undone!*)

"How far is St. Helena from the Beresina ice?"
An ill way—a chill way—the ice begins to crack.
But not so far for gentlemen who never took advice.
(*When you can't go forward you must e'en come back!*)

(176)

"How far is St. Helena from the field of Waterloo?"
A near way—a clear way—the ship will take you soon.
A pleasant place for gentlemen with little left to do.
(*Morning never tries you until the afternoon!*)

"How far from St. Helena to the Gate of Heaven's Grace?"
That no one knows—that no one knows—and no one ever will.
But fold your hands across your heart and cover up your face,
And after all your traipsings, child, lie still.

Born 1769 at Ajaccio in Corsica, Napoleon Bonaparte. This, with its light tracing of the fatality of power, may well be the best of Kipling's lyrics.

A.D. 1770

From THE DESERTED VILLAGE

by Oliver Goldsmith

Sweet Auburn! loveliest village of the plain,
Where health and plenty cheered the laboring swain,
Where smiling spring its earliest visit paid,
And parting summer's lingering blooms delayed;
Dear lovely bowers of innocence and ease,
Seats of my youth, when every sport could please,
How often have I loitered o'er thy green,
Where humble happiness endeared every scene!
How often have I paused on every charm,
The sheltered cot, the cultivated farm,
The never-failing brook, the busy mill,
The decent church that topped the neighboring hill,
The hawthorn bush, with seats beneath the shade,
For talking age and whispering lovers made!
How often have I blessed the coming day,
When toil remitting lent its turn to play,
And all the village train, from labor free,
Led up their sports beneath the spreading tree,
While many a pastime circled in the shade,
The young contending as the old surveyed;
And many a gambol frolicked o'er the ground,
And sleights of art and feats of strength went round!
And still, as each repeated pleasure tired,
Succeeding sports the mirthful band inspired;
The dancing pair that simply sought renown,
By holding out to tire each other down;
The swain mistrustless of his smutted face,
While secret laughter tittered round the place;
The bashful virgin's sidelong looks of love,

The matron's glance that would those looks reprove:
These were thy charms, sweet village! Sports like these,
With sweet succession, taught even toil to please;
These round thy bowers their cheerful influence shed;
These were thy charms—but all these charms are fled.
  Sweet smiling village, loveliest of the lawn,
Thy sports are fled and all thy charms withdrawn:
Amidst thy bowers the tyrant's hand is seen,
And desolation saddens all thy green;
One only master grasps the whole domain,
And half a tillage stints thy smiling plain.
No more thy glassy brook reflects the day,
But choked with sedges, works its weedy way;
Along thy glades, a solitary guest,
The hollow-sounding bittern guards its nest;
Amidst thy desert walks the lapwing flies,
And tires their echoes with unvaried cries;
Sunk are thy bowers in shapeless ruin all,
And the long grass o'er-tops the moldering wall;
And trembling, shrinking from the spoiler's hand,
Far, far away, thy children leave the land.

  Ill fares the land, to hastening ills a prey,
Where wealth accumulates, and men decay.
Princes and lords may flourish, or may fade—
A breath can make them, as a breath has made;
But a bold peasantry, their country's pride,
When once destroyed, can never be supplied.

❧

*Absentee landlords, Englishmen, or Irishmen living away from their
lands, helped bring about the rural decay Goldsmith chronicles. There
was no lure to working someone else's land for the younger generation and the Irish were beginning their long history of emigration—
to the United States as well as to England—that reached its peak in
the terrible years of potato famine in the 1840's.*

(179)

A.D. 1770

CAPTAIN COOK, from RANOLF AND AMOHIA

by Alfred Domett

The ruder Italy laid bare
   By that keen searcher of the Seas,
Whose tempest-baffling, never baffled keel,
Left half our planet little to reveal;
   But restless roaming everywhere
Zigzagged the vast Pacific as he prest
With godlike patience his benignant quest;
True hero-god, who realized the notion
Its races feign of mythic Maui still,
And plucked up with a giant might of will
A hundred islands from Oblivion's ocean!
Sea-king and sage—staunch huntsman of pure Fame,
Beating the waste of waters for his game,
Untrodden shores or tribes without a name;
   That nothing in an island's shape,
   Mist-muffled peak or faint cloud-cape,
Might his determined thoughtful glance escape;
   No virgin lands he left unknown,
   Where future Englands might be sown,
   And nations noble as his own.

❦

Captain James Cook was addicted to exploring as other men have been to drugs or the bottle. He uncovered much of the Pacific that had been untouched or uncharted before (including New Zealand, the ruder Italy mentioned above) and met his death at the hands of Hawaiian islanders in 1779.

THE FRENCH REVOLUTION AS IT APPEARED TO ENTHUSIASTS AT ITS COMMENCEMENT

by William Wordsworth

Oh! pleasant exercise of hope and joy!
For mighty were the auxiliars which then stood
Upon our side, we who were strong in love!
Bliss was it in that dawn to be alive,
But to be young was very heaven!—Oh! times,
In which the meager, stale, forbidding ways
Of custom, law, and statute, took at once
The attraction of a country in romance!
When Reason seemed the most to assert her rights,
When most intent on making of herself
A prime Enchantress—to assist the work
Which then was going forward in her name!
Not favored spots alone, but the whole earth,
The beauty wore of promise, that which sets
(As at some moment might not be unfelt
Among the bowers of Paradise itself)
The budding rose above the rose full blown.
What temper at the prospect did not wake
To happiness unthought of? The inert
Were roused, and lively natures rapt away!
They who had fed their childhood upon dreams,
The playfellows of fancy, who had made
All powers of swiftness, subtilty and strength
Their ministers,—who in lordly wise had stirred
Among the grandest objects of the sense,
And dealt with whatsoever they found there
As if they had within some lurking right
To wield it;—they, too, who, of gentle mood,

Had watched all gentle motions, and to these
Had fitted their own thoughts, schemers more mild,
And in the region of their peaceful selves;—
Now was it that both found, the meek and lofty
Did both find helpers to their hearts' desire,
And stuff at hand, plastic as they could wish;
Were called upon to exercise their skill,
Not in Utopia, subterranean fields,
Or some secreted island, Heaven knows where!
But in the very world, which is the world
Of all of us,—the place where in the end
We find our happiness, or not at all!

❧

When France turned on a corrupt and inept monarchy, it seemed
a dawn of new hope not merely to Wordsworth, but to progressive-
minded thinkers all through Europe. It was a quick and sad disillu-
sion to romantic sympathizers when factionist revolutionaries began
killing each other and the whole great dream ended ten years later
with the consulate, then the dictatorship of Napoleon I.

A.D. 1793

LET THE BROTHELS OF PARIS BE OPENED

by William Blake

"Let the brothels of Paris be opened
With many an alluring dance
To awake Pestilence thro' the city,"
Said the beautiful Queen of France.

The King woke on his couch of gold,
As soon as he heard these tidings told:
"Arise & come, both fife & drum,
And the Famine shall eat both crust & crumb."

Then he swore a great & solemn Oath:
"To kill the people I am loath,
But If they rebel, they must go to hell:
They shall have a Priest & a passing bell."

Then old Nobodaddy aloft
Farted & belched & cough'd,
And said, "I love hanging & drawing & quartering
Every bit as well as war & slaughtering.
Damn praying & singing,
Unless they will bring in
The blood of ten thousand by fighting or swinging."

The Queen of France just touched this Globe,
And the Pestilence darted from her robe;
But our good Queen quite grows to the ground,
And a great many suckers grow all around.

Fayette beside King Lewis stood;
He saw him sign his hand;

(183)

And soon he saw the famine rage
About the fruitful land.

Fayette beheld the Queen to smile
And wink her lovely eye;
And soon he saw the pestilence
From street to street to fly.

Fayette beheld the King & Queen
In tears & iron bound;
But mute Fayette wept tear for tear,
And guarded them around.

Fayette, Fayette, thou'rt bought & sold,
And sold is thy happy morrow;
Thou gavest the tears of Pity away
In exchange for tears of sorrow.

Who will exchange his own fire side
For the steps of another's door?
Who will exchange his wheaten loaf
For the links of a dungeon floor?

O, who would smile on the wintry seas,
& Pity the stormy roar?
Or who will exchange his new born child
For the dog at the wintry door?

❧

Blake's political comments were as prophetically arcane as the rest of
his verse, but it is at least possible to assume that he did not love
the King and Queen of France. Fayette is the Marquis de La Fayette,
supporter of American Republicanism in the American Revolution,
uneasy compromiser in that of his own nation. He was active in the
first period of the French Revolution, but favored a constitutional
monarchy. He had to flee France in 1792 and was clapped into
Austrian and Prussian prisons until Napoleon arranged his release in
1797.

A.D. 1794

TO TOUSSAINT L'OUVERTURE

by William Wordsworth

Toussaint, the most unhappy Man of Men!
Whether the whistling Rustic tend his plough
Within they hearing, or thy head be now
Pillowed in some deep dungeon's earless den;—
O miserable Chieftan! where and when
Wilt thou find patience? Yet due not; do thou
Wear rather in thy bonds a chearful brow:
Though fallen Thyself, never to rise again,
Live, and take comfort. Thou hast left behind
Powers that will work for thee: air, earth and skies;
There's not a breathing of the common wind
That will forget thee; thou hast great allies;
Thy friends are exultations, agonies,
And love, and Man's unconquerable mind.

❦

The inspirational fires of the American and French Revolutions spread far and wide, even to the French colonial island of Haiti in the West Indies. Toussaint, a prime mover in the revolt did not last long; Henri Christophe, dubbing himself Henri I, took over as dictator and dictators of one sort or another the unhappy island has had ever since.

A.D. 1797

SAPPHICS

The Friend of Humanity and the Knife-grinder

by George Canning

Friend of Humanity:
Needy Knife-grinder! whither are you going?
Rough is the road, your wheel is out of order—
Bleak blows the blast; your hat has got a hole in't,
                    So have your breeches!

Weary Knife-grinder! little think the proud ones,
Who as their coaches roll along the turnpike-
road, what hard work 'tis crying all day "Knives and
                    Scissors to grind O!"

Tell me, Knife-grinder, how came you to grind knives?
Did some rich man tyrannically use you?
Was it the squire? or parson of the parish?
                    Or the attorney?

Was it the squire, for killing of his game? or
Covetous parson, for his tithes distraining?
Or roguish lawyer, made you lose your little
                    All in a lawsuit?

(Have you not read the Rights of Man, by Tom Paine?)
Drops of compassion tremble on my eyelids,
Ready to fall, as soon as you have told your
                    Pitiful story.

KNIFE-GRINDER:

Story! God bless you! I have none to tell, sir,
Only last night a-drinking at the Chequers,
This poor old hat and breeches, as you see, were
>Torn in a scuffle.

Constables came up for to take me into
Custody; they took me before the justice;
Justice Oldmixon put me in the parish-
>Stocks for a vagrant.

I should be glad to drink your Honor's health in
A pot of beer, if you will give me sixpence;
But for my part, I never love to meddle
>With politics, sir.

FRIEND OF HUMANITY:

I give you sixpence! I will see thee damned first—
Wretch! whom no sense of wrongs can rouse to vengeance—
Sordid, unfeeling, reprobate, degraded,
>Spiritless outcast!

(Kicks the Knife-grinder, overturns his wheel, and exits in a transport
of Republican enthusiasm and universal philanthropy.)

Canning served England twice as Foreign Secretary and finally as
Prime Minister (in 1827), a staunch, but not stupid Conservative.
These verses parody some sapphics (a verse form based on the Grecian
meters of Sappho) by Robert Southey. To Conservatives of Canning's day, the term Republican was used as loosely (and as wildly
and pejoratively) as Communist is used by right-wing politicos today.
The "Friend of Humanity" was one George Tierney, a reform-minded
member of Parliament. Tom Paine's Rights of Man was the pamphlet
by the famed American radical.

A.D. 1797

ON THE EXTINCTION OF THE VENETIAN REPUBLIC

by William Wordsworth

Once did She hold the gorgeous East in fee;
And was the safeguard of the West; the worth
Of Venice did not fall below her birth,
Venice, the eldest Child of Liberty.
She was a Maiden City, bright and free;
No guile seduced, no force could violate;
And when She took unto herself a Mate,
She must espouse the everlasting Sea.
And what if she had seen those glories fade,
Those titles vanish, and that strength decay;
Yet shall some tribute of regret be paid
When her long life hath reached its final day:
Men are we, and must grieve when even the Shade
Of that which once was great, is passed away.

❦

There was no room for semi-feudal city-states, however glorious their past, in the new Europe that began to unfold from the French Revolution. Napoleon, the genius general of the new French Directory, accepted the abdication of the last Doge and then cheerfully let Venice be turned over to Austria by the Treaty of Campo Formio.

A.D. 1798

CASABIANCA

by Felicia Hemans

The boy stood on the burning deck,
    Whence all but he had fled;
The flame that lit the battle's wreck
    Shone round him o'er the dead.

Yet beautiful and bright he stood,
    As born to rule the storm;
A creature of heroic blood,
    A proud, though childlike form.

The flames rolled on; he would not go
    Without his father's word;
That father, faint in death below,
    His voice no longer heard.

He called aloud, "Say, father, say
    If yet my task be done!"
He knew not that the chieftain lay
    Unconscious of his son.

"Speak, father!" once again he cried,
    "If I may yet be gone!"
And but the booming shots replied,
    And fast the flames rolled on.

Upon his brow he felt their breath,
    And in his waving hair,
And looked from that lone post of death
    In still yet brave despair;

And shouted but once more aloud,
  "My father, must I stay?"
While o'er him, fast, through sail and shroud
  The wreathing fires made way.

They wrapped the ship in splendor wild,
  They caught the flag on high,
And streamed above the gallant child,
  Like banners in the sky.

There came a burst of thunder sound;
  The boy,—oh! where was he?
Ask of the winds, that far around
  With fragments strewed the sea,—

With mast, and helm, and pennon fair,
  That well had borne their part,—
But the noblest thing that perished there,
  Was that young, faithful heart.

❧

It comes as a shock to some otherwise educated people to learn that the boy who stood on the burning deck was a real person. Louis de Casabianca was captain of the French warship, L'Orient, at the battle of the Nile. The British naval genius, Horatio Nelson, made burning mincemeat of the French fleet and the junior Casabianca's name is about all that is left to memorialize it.

A.D. 1800

HOHENLINDEN

by Thomas Campbell

On Linden, when the sun was low,
All bloodless lay the untrodden snow;
As dark as winter was the flow
    Of Iser, rolling rapidly.

But Linden saw another sight,
When the drum beat at dead of night
Commanding fires of death to light
    The darkness of her scenery.

By torch and trumpet fast arrayed
Each horseman drew his battle blade,
And furious every charger neighed
    To join the dreadful revelry.

Then shook the hills with thunder riven,
Then rushed the steed to battle driven,
And louder than the bolts of heaven
    Far flashed the red artillery.

But redder yet that light shall glow
On Linden's hills of a stainéd snow,
And bloodier yet the torrent flow
    Of Iser, rolling rapidly.

'Tis morn, but scarce yon level sun
Can pierce the war clouds, rolling dun,
Where furious Frank and fiery Hun
    Shout in their sulphurous canopy.

The combat deepens. On, ye brave
Who rush to glory, or the grave!
Wave, Munich! all thy banners wave,
    And charge with all thy chivalry!

Few, few, shall part, where many meet!
The snow shall be their winding-sheet,
And every turf beneath their feet
    Shall be a soldier's sepulcher.

✿

Jean Victor Moreau, a French general of Napoleon's Consulate, defeated the Archduke John of Austria decisively at Hohenlinden and Austria was forced to make peace with the upstart, post-revolutionary French. Moreau lasted four more years until he was implicated in a plot against Napoleon (then on the verge of declaring himself Emperor) and had to flee to America.

THE BATTLE OF THE BALTIC

by Thomas Campbell

Of Nelson and the North
Sing the glorious day's renown,
When to battle fierce came forth
All the might of Denmark's crown,
And her arms along the deep proudly shone:
By each gun the lighted brand
In a bold determined hand,
And the Prince of all the land
Led them on.

Like leviathans afloat
Lay their bulwarks on the brine,
While the sign of battle flew
On the lofty British line:
It was ten of April morn by the chime:
As they drifted on their path
There was silence deep as death,
And the boldest held his breath
For a time.

But the might of England flushed
To anticipate the scene:
And her van the fleeter rushed
O'er the deadly space between:
"Hearts of oak!" our captain cried, when each gun
From its adamantine lips
Spread a death-shade round the ships,
Like the hurricane eclipse
Of the sun.

Again! again! again!
And the havoc did not slack,
Till a feeble cheer the Dane
To our cheering sent us back;—
Their shots along the deep slowly boom:—
Then ceased—and all is wail,
As they strike the shattered sail,
Or in conflagration pale
Light the gloom.

Out spoke the victor then
As he hailed them o'er the wave:
"Ye are brothers; ye are men!
And we conquer but to save:—
So peace instead of death let us bring:
But yield, proud foe, thy fleet,
With the crews at England's feet,
And make submission meet
To our king." . . .

Now joy, old England, raise!
For the tidings of thy might,
By the festal cities' blaze,
While the wine-cup shines in light!
And yet amidst that joy and uproar,
Let us think of them that sleep
Full many a fathom deep,
By thy wild and stormy steep,
Elsinore!

Brave hearts! to Britain's pride
Once so faithful and so true,
On the deck of fame that died
With the gallant good Riou:
Soft sigh the winds of Heaven o'er their grave!

While the billow mournful rolls
And the mermaid's song condoles,
Singing glory to the souls
Of the brave!

❦

Campbell manages to make a patriotic hymn out of a rather unpleasant chapter in British naval history which included the destructive bombardment of a virtually undefended Copenhagen.

A.D. 1806

NELSON AND PITT *from* MARMION

by Sir Walter Scott

To mute and material things
New life revolving summer brings;
The genial call dead Nature hears,
And in her glory reappears.
But O my country's wintry state
What second spring can renovate?
What powerful call shall bid arise
The buried warlike and the wise;
The mind that thought for Britain's weal,
The hand that grasped the victor's steel?
The vernal sun new life bestows
Even on the meanest flower that blows:
But vainly, vainly may he shine,
Where glory weeps o'er Nelson's shrine;
And vainly pierce the solemn gloom,
That shrouds, O Pitt, thy hallowed tomb!

Deep graved in every British heart,
O never let those names depart!
Say to your sons,—Lo, here his grave,
Who victor died on Gadite wave;
To him, as to the burning levin,
Short, bright, resistless course was given.
Where'er his country's foes were found
Was heard the fated thunder's sound,
Till burst, the bolt on yonder shore,
Rolled, blazed, destroyed,—and was no more.

Nor mourn ye less his perished worth,
Who bade the conqueror go forth,
And launched that thunderbolt of war
On Egypt, Hafnia, Trafalgar;
Who, born to guide such high emprise,
For Britain's weal was early wise;
Alas! to whom the Almighty gave,
For Britain's sins an early grave!
His worth, who in his mightiest hour
A bauble held the pride of power,
Spurned at the sordid lust of pelf,
And served his Albion for herself;
Who, when the frantic crowd amain
Strained at subjection's bursting rein,
O'er their wild mood full conquest gained
The pride he would not crush restrained,
Showed their fierce zeal a worthier cause,
And brought the freeman's arm to aid the freeman's laws.

THE BURIAL OF SIR JOHN MOORE

by Charles Wolfe

Not a drum was heard, not a funeral note,
　As his corse to the rampart we hurried;
Not a soldier discharged his farewell shot
　O'er the grave where our hero we buried.

We buried him darkly at dead of night,
　The sods with our bayonets turning,
By the struggling moonbeam's misty light
　And the lanthorn dimly burning.

No useless coffin enclosed his breast,
　Not in sheet or in shroud we wound him;
But he lay like a warrior taking his rest
　With his martial cloak around him.

Few and short were the prayers we said,
　And we spoke not a word of sorrow;
But we steadfastly gazed on the face that was dead,
　And we bitterly thought of the morrow.

We thought, as we hollowed his narrow bed
　And smoothed down his lonely pillow,
That the foe and the stranger would tread o'er his head,
　And we far away on the billow!

Lightly they'll talk of the spirit that's gone,
　And o'er his cold ashes upbraid him;
But little he'll reck, if they let him sleep on
　In the grave where a Briton has laid him.

But half our weary task was done
   When the clock struck the note for retiring;
And we heard the distant and random gun
   That the foe was sullenly firing.

Slowly and sadly we laid him down,
   From the field of his fame fresh and gory;
We carved not a line, and we raised not a stone,
   But we left him alone with his glory.

❦

Marshal Soult's French forces vanquished the British at Corunna where the English commander Sir John Moore was killed. Despite such conventional military triumph, the French were never able to stamp out continuing guerrilla resistance.

A.D. 1809

HOFFER

by William Wordsworth

Of mortal parents is the Hero born
By whom the undaunted Tyrolese are led?
Or is it Tell's great Spirit, from the dead
Returned to animate an age forlorn?
He comes like Phoebus through the gates of morn
When dreary darkness is discomfitted,
Yet mark his modest state! upon his head,
That simple crest, a heron's plume, is worn.
O Liberty! they stagger at the shock
From van to rear—and with one mind would flee,
But half their host is buried:—rock on rock
Descends!—beneath this godlike Warrior, see!
Hills, torrents, woods, embodied to bemock
The Tyrant, and confound his cruelty.

❦

Andreas Hoffer (or Hofer) led local resistance to Napoleon in the
Austrian Tyrol. His followers put up a brave struggle, but they could
not win against the overpowering force of the French and Napoleon's
Bavarian allies. Hofer was compelled to flee; the French caught him
and executed him at Mantua in Italy.

A.D. 1812

THE MARCH TO MOSCOW

by Robert Southey

The Emperor Nap he would set off
On a summer excursion to Moscow;
The fields were green and the sky was blue,
   Morbleu! Parbleu!
What a splendid excursion to Moscow!

The Emperor Nap he talk'd so big
   That he frighten'd Mr. Roscoe.
And Counsellor Brougham was all in a fume
   At the thought of the march to Moscow:
The Russians, he said, they were undone,
   And the great Fee-Faw-Fum
     Would presently come,
With a hop, step, and jump, unto London,
   For, as to his conquering Russia,
   However some people might scoff it,
   Do it he could, do it he would,
And from doing it nothing would come but good,
   And nothing would call him off it.

But the Russians stoutly they turned to
   Upon the road to Moscow.
Nap had to fight his way all through;
They could fight, though they could not parlez-vous;
But the fields were green and the sky was blue,
   Morbleu! Parbleu!
   And so he got to Moscow.

He found the place too warm for him,
    For they set fire to Moscow,
To get there had cost him much ado,
And then no better course he knew
While the fields were green and the sky was blue,
    Morbleu! Parbleu!
  But to march back again from Moscow.

The Russians they stuck close to him
    All on the road from Moscow—
And Shouvaloff he shovell'd them off,
And Markoff he mark'd them off,
And Krosnoff he cross'd them off,
And Touchkoff he touch'd them off,
And Boroskoff he bored them off,
And Kutousoff he cut them off,
And Parenzoff he pared them off,
And Doctoroff he doctor'd them off,
And Rodinoff he flogged them off,
And last of all, an Admiral came,
A terrible man with a terrible name,
A name which you all know by sight very well,
But which no one can speak, and no one can spell.

And then came on the frost and snow
    All on the road from Moscow.
Worse and worse every day the elements grew,
The fields were so white and the sky was so blue.
    Sacreblue! Ventrebleu!
  What a horrible journey from Moscow!

Too cold upon the road was he;
Too hot he had been in Moscow;
But colder and hotter he still may be,
For the grave is colder than Muscovy;

And a place there is to be kept in view,
Where the fire is red, and the brimstone blue,
      Morbleu! Parbleu!
But there he must stay for a very long day,
For from thence there is no stealing away,
   As there was on the road from Moscow.

❦

Southey's bouncey doggerel verses have the exultant yap familiar at
the fall of any giant, good giant or bad, yet manage a suggestion of
the bleak horror of the Russian campaign. Within present memories
is Hitler's equally disastrous attempt on Russia (as well as—stanza
two—the "well-informed opinions" that Russia could never withstand
him). Southey's rhyming of French curses—morbleu with blue—sug-
gests that British pronunciation of French in 1812 matches American
assaults on the same tongue today. Same comment for the puns on
names of Russian generals in stanza five.

A.D. 1815

WATERLOO EVE from CHILDE HAROLD

by George Gordon, Lord Byron

There was a sound of revelry by night,
And Belgium's capital had gathered then
Her Beauty and her Chivalry, and bright
The lamps shone o'er fair women and brave men;
A thousand hearts beat happily; and when
Music arose with its voluptuous swell,
Soft eyes looked love to eyes which spake again,
And all went merry as a marriage bell;
But hush! hark! a deep sound strikes like a rising knell!

Did ye not hear it?—No; 'twas but the wind,
Or the car rattling o'er the stony street;
On with the dance! let joy be unconfined;
No sleep till morn, when Youth and Pleasure meet
To chase the glowing Hours with flying feet—
But hark!—that heavy sound breaks in once more
As if the clouds its echo would repeat;
And nearer, clearer, deadlier than before!
Arm! Arm! it is—it is—the cannon's opening roar!

*   *   *   *

Ah! then and there was hurrying to and fro,
And gathering tears, and tremblings of distress,
And cheeks all pale, which but an hour ago
Blushed at the praise of their own loveliness;
And there were sudden partings, such as press
The life from out young hearts, and choking sighs
Which ne'er might be repeated; who could guess
If ever more should meet those mutual eyes,
Since upon night so sweet such awful morn could rise!

And there was mounting in hot haste: the steed,
The mustering squadron, and the clattering car,
Went pouring forward with impetuous speed,
And swiftly forming in the ranks of war;
And the deep thunder peal on peal afar;
And near, the beat of the alarming drum
Roused up the soldier ere the morning star;
While thronged the citizens with terror dumb,
Or whispering, with white lips—"The foe, they come! they
    come!"

*   *   *   *

Last noon beheld them full of lusty life,
Last eve in Beauty's circle proudly gay,
The midnight brought the signal-sound of strife,
The morn the marshaling in arms—the day
Battle's magnificently stern array!
The thunderclouds close o'er it, which when rent,
The earth is covered thick with other clay,
Which her own clay shall cover, heaped and spent,
Rider and horse—friend, foe—in one red burial blent!

A.D. 1819

From THE MASQUE OF ANARCHY

by Percy Bysshe Shelley

As I lay asleep in Italy
There came a voice from over the Sea,
And with great power it forth led me
To walk in the vision of Poesy.

I met Murder on the way—
He had a mask like Castlereagh—
Very smooth he looked, yet grim;
Seven blood-hounds followed him:

All were fat; and well they might
Be in admirable plight,
For one by one, and two by two,
He tossed them human hearts to chew
Which from his wide cloak he drew.

Next came Fraud, and he had on,
Like Eldon, an ermined gown;
His big tears, for he wept well,
Turned to mill-stones as they fell.

And the little children, who
Round his knees played to and fro,
Thinking every tear a gem,
Had their brains knocked out by them.

Clothed with the Bible, as with light,
And the shadows of the night,

(206)

Like Sidmouth, next, Hypocrisy
On a crocodile rode by.

And many more Destructions played
In this ghastly masquerade,
All disguised, even to the eyes,
Like Bishops, lawyers, peers, or spies.

Last came Anarchy: he rode
On a white horse splashed with blood;
He was pale even to his lips,
Like Death in the Apocalypse.

And he wore a kingly crown;
And in his grasp a sceptre shone;
On his brow this mark I saw—
"I AM GOD, AND KING, AND LAW!"

❧

*Shelley's anger sparked into flame at news of the Peterloo Massacre
in Manchester where troops had fired into an unarmed crowd gathered to plead for reform of Parliament. Castlereagh was Foreign Secretary and a symbol of reaction; Eldon and Sidmouth were other government figures. There are 82 more stanzas, well worth reading.*

A.D. 1823

MARCO BOZZARIS

by Fitz-Greene Halleck

At midnight, in his guarded tent,
   The Turk was dreaming of the hour
When Greece, her knee in suppliance bent,
   Should tremble at his power.
In dreams, through camp and court, he bore
The trophies of a conqueror;
   In dreams his song of triumph heard;
Then wore his monarch's signet-ring,
Then pressed that monarch's throne—a king;
As wild his thoughts, and gay of wing,
   As Eden's garden bird.

At midnight, in the forest shades,
   Bozzaris ranged his Suliote band,—
True as the steel of their tried blades,
   Heroes in heart and hand.
There had the Persian's thousands stood,
There had the glad earth drunk their blood,
   On old Plataea's day;
And now there breathed that haunted air
The sons of sires who conquered there,
With arms to strike, and soul to dare,
   As quick, as far, as they.

An hour passed on, the Turk awoke:
   That bright dream was his last;
He woke—to hear his sentries shriek,
   "To arms! They come! the Greek! the Greek!"
He woke—to die midst flame, and smoke,

And shout, and groan, and sabre-stroke,
　And death-shots falling thick and fast
As lightnings from the mountain-cloud;
And heard with voice as trumpet loud,
　Bozzaris cheer his band:
"Strike—till the last armed foe expires;
Strike—for your altars and your fires;
Strike—for the green graves of your sires,
　God, and your native land!"

They fought—like brave men, long and well;
　They piled that ground with Moslem slain:
They conquered—but Bozzaris fell,
　Bleeding at every vein.
His few surviving comrades saw
His smile when rang their proud hurrah,
　And the red field was won;
Then saw in death his eyelids close
Calmly as to a night's repose
　Like flowers at set of sun.

Come to the bridal chamber, death,
　Come to the mother's, when she feels,
For the first time, her first-born's breath
　Come when the blessed seals
That close the pestilence are broke,
And crowded cities wail its stroke;
Come in consumption's ghastly form,
The earthquake shock, the ocean storm;
Come when the heart beats high and warm,
　With banquet song and dance and wine,—
And thou art terrible; the tear,
The groan, the knell, the pall, the bier,
And all we know, or dream, or fear
　Of agony, are thine.

But to the hero, when his sword
  Has won the battle for the free,
Thy voice sounds like a prophet's word,
And in its hollow tones are heard
  The thanks of millions yet to be.
Come when the task of fame is wrought;
Come with her laurel-leaf, blood-bought;
  Come in her crowning hour,—and then
Thy sunken eye's unearthly light
To him is welcome as the sight
  Of sky and stars to prisoned men;
Thy grasp is welcome as the hand
Of brother in a foreign land;
Thy summons welcome as the cry
That told the Indian isles were nigh
  To the world-seeking Genoese,
When the land-wind, from woods of palm,
And orange-groves, and fields of balm,
  Blew o'er the Haytian seas.

Bozzaris! with the storied brave
  Greece nurtured in her glory's time,
Rest thee; there is no prouder grave,
  Even in her own proud clime.
She wore no funeral wreathes for thee,
  Nor bade the dark hearse weave its plume,
Like torn branch from death's leafless tree,
In sorrow's pomp and pageantry,
  The heartless luxury of the tomb.
But she remembers thee as one
Long loved, and for a season gone.
For thee her poet's lyre is wreathed,
Her marble wrought, her music breathed;
For thee she rings the birthday bells;
Of thee her babes' first lisping tells;

For thine her evening prayer is said
At palace, couch and cottage bed.
Her soldier, closing with the foe,
Gives for thy sake a deadlier blow;
His plighted maiden, when she fears
For him, the joy of her young years,
Thinks of thy fate, and checks her tears.
    And she, the mother of thy boys,
Though in her eye and faded cheek
Is read the grief she will not speak,
    The memory of her buried joys,—
And even she who gave thee birth,—
Will, by her pilgrim-circled hearth,
    Talk of thy doom without a sigh;
For thou art freedom's now, and fame's,—
One of the few, the immortal names
    That were not born to die.

❧

Marco Bozzaris, a leader in the Greek struggle against Turkish rule,
was killed in a night raid on the Turkish camp at Laspi (the site of
Ancient Greek Plataea). His raid was successful and he is said to have
died saying: "To die for liberty is a pleasure and not a pain." Despite
Fitz-Halleck's tribute and its high closing hopes, I have still to meet
a Greek who has ever heard of Marco Bozzaris, but I am still looking.

A.D. 1824

GREEK WAR SONG

translated from the Greek of Riga
by Lord Byron

Sons of the Greeks, arise!
The glorious hour's gone forth,
And, worthy of such ties,
Display who gave us birth.

> Sons of Greeks! let us go
> In arms against the foe,
> Till their hated blood shall flow
> In a river past our feet.

Then manfully despising
The Turkish tyrant's yoke,
Let your country see you rising,
And all her chains are broke.
Brave shades of chiefs and sages,
Behold the coming strife!
Hellenes of past ages,
Oh, start again to life!
At the sound of my trumpet, breaking
Your sleep, oh, join with me!
And the seven-hill'd city seeking,
Fight, conquer, till we're free.

Chorus

Sparta, Sparta, why in slumbers
Lethargic dost thou lie?

Awake, and join they numbers
With Athens, old ally!
Leonidas recalling,
That chief of ancient song,
Who saved ye once from falling,
The terrible! the strong!
Who made that bold diversion
In old Thermopylae,
And warring with the Persian
To keep his country free;
With his three hundred waging
The battle, long he stood,
And like a lion raging,
Expired in seas of blood.

Chorus

❦

Greece joined the struggle for national independence, in its case
from the Turkish yoke. Byron found in Greece the perfect wedding
of two of his great loves, ancient classicism and modern freedom. He
died there, trying to help insurgent Greek forces.

A.D. 1827

THE GLORIOUS VICTORY OF NAVARINO

Anonymous

Come all you British hearts of oak, and listen unto me,
While I relate the famous fight now crown'd with victory,
When the Turkish and Egyptian Fleet were taught the truth
   again,
That Britons still and ever will be champions on the main.

Chorus

Then drink a health to Codrington—to Codrington huzza!
Who did destroy the Turkish fleet in Navarino Bay.

On the twentieth of October the glorious work began,
Bold Ibrahim vainly boasted that he'd slaughter ev'ry man,
But Codrington resolved the *Asia* should display
A bright example to the rest, and he would lead the way.

The *Genoa* and the *Albion* he placed by his side,
And near to him De Rigney, commander of th' *Armide*,
The *Glasgow* and the *Cambrian*, the *Dartmouth* & the *Rose*
Were placed in fine order alongside of their foes.

The proud Egyptians vainly said our fleet by far outvies
The boasting little squadron that's mann'd by the Allies,
They fired into the *Asia*, a signal for the fray,
But instantly brave Codrington a broadside did display.

O then it was a glorious sight, which Britons do admire.
From ship to ship most gallantly began a raking fire,
The Turkish and Egyptian fleet, by British tars employ'd,
Roll one by one until the whole completely was destroy'd.

(214)

Then Briton fill a bumper to the memory of the slain,
Who fell defending of our rights upon the stormy main,
To the French and Russian Admirals, whom Codrington did aid,
And to the men on board each ship who courage have displayed.

From THE RISING VILLAGE

by Oliver Goldsmith

What noble courage must their hearts have fired,
How great the ardor which their souls inspired,
Who, leaving far behind their native plain,
Have sought a home beyond the western main;
And braved the terrors of stormy seas,
In search of wealth, of freedom, and of ease!
Oh! none can tell but they who sadly share
The bosom's anguish, and its wild despair,
What dire distress awaits the hardy bands
That venture first on bleak and desert lands;
How great the pain, the danger, and the toil
Which marks the first rude culture of the soil.
When, looking round, the lonely settler sees
His home amid a wilderness of trees;
How sinks his heart in those deep solitudes,
When not a voice upon his ear intrudes;
Where solemn silence all the waste pervades,
Heightening the horror of its gloomy shades . . .

While now the Rising Village claims a name,
Its limits, still increase and still its fame,
The wand'ring pedlar, who undaunted traced
His lonely footsteps o'er the silent waste;
Who traversed once the cold and snow-clad plain,
Reckless of danger, trouble, or of pain,
To find a market for his little wares,
The source of all his hopes and all his cares,
Establish'd here, his settled home maintains,
And soon a merchant's higher title gains.

(216)

Around his store, on spacious shelves array'd,
Behold his great and various stock in trade!
Here nails and blankets, side by side, are seen,
There, horses' collars and a large tureen;
Buttons and tumblers, codhooks, spoons and knives,
Shawls for young damsels, flannels for old wives;
Woolcards and stockings, hats for men and boys,
Mill-saws and fenders, silks, and infant toys;
All useful things and joined with many more,
Compose the well-assorted country store . . .

The half-breed Doctor next here settles down,
And hopes the village soon will prove a town.
No rival here disputes his rustic skill,
He cures, by chance, or ends each human ill:
By turns he physics, or his patients bleeds,
Uncertain in what case each best succeeds.
And if, from friends untimely snatch'd away,
Some beauty fall a victim to decay;
If some fine youth, his parents' fond delight,
Be early hurried to the shades of night;
Death bears the blame, 'tis his envenom'd dart
That strikes the suff'ring mortal to the heart . . .

❧

*Sixty years after The Deserted Village, another Oliver Goldsmith,
grandnephew of the first one, wrote his own verses about the settlers
who had come to Canada to escape the pall fallen on free land in
Ireland, England, and Scotland.*

A.D. 1837

QUEEN VICTORIA

Anonymous

Welcome now, Victoria!
Welcome to the throne!
May all the trades begin to stir,
   Now you are Queen of England;
For your most gracious Majesty,
May see what wretched poverty,
Is to be found on England's ground,
   Now you are Queen of England.

While o'er the country you preside,
Providence will be your guide,
The people then will never chide
   Victoria, Queen of England.
She doth declare it her intent
To extend reform in Parliament,
On doing good she's firmly bent,
   While she is Queen of England.

Says she, I'll try my utmost skill,
That the poor people have their fill;
Forsake them!—no, I never will,
   When I am Queen of England.
For oft my mother said to me,
Let this your study always be,
To see the people blest and free,
   Should you be Queen of England.

And now, my daughter, you do reign,
Much opposition to sustain,

You'll surely have before you gain
  The blessings of Old England.
O yes, dear mother, that is true,
I know my sorrows won't be few
Poor people shall have work to do,
  When I am Queen of England.

I will encourage every trade,
For their labor must be paid,
In this free country then she said,
  Victoria, Queen of England;
That poor-law bill, with many more,
Shall be trampled on the floor—
The rich must keep the helpless poor,
  While I am Queen of England.

The Royal Queen of Britain's isle
Soon will make the people smile,
Her heart none can the least defile,
  Victoria, Queen of England.
Although she is of early years,
She is possess'd of tender cares,
To wipe away the orphan's tears,
  While she is Queen of England.

With joy each Briton doth exclaim,
Both far and near across the main,
Victoria we now proclaim
  The Royal Queen of England;
Long may she live, and happy be,
Adorn'd with robes of Royalty,
With blessings from her subjects free,
  While she is Queen of England.

In every town and village gay,
The bells shall ring, and music play,
Upon her Coronation Day,
　　Victoria, Queen of England.
While her affections we do win,
And every day fresh blessings bring,
Ladies, help me for to sing,
　　Victoria, Queen of England.

A.D. 1840

SIBERIA

by James Clarence Mangan

In Siberia's wastes
The ice-wind's breath
Woundeth like toothèd steel:
Lost Siberia doth reveal
Only blight and death.

Blight and death alone.
No summer shines;
Night is interblent with day;
In Siberia's wastes, alway
The blood blackens, the heart pines.

In Siberia's wastes
No tears are shed,
For they freeze within the brain,
Naught is felt but dullest pain,
Pain acute, yet dead;

Pain as in a dream,
When years go by
Funeral-paced yet fugitive;
When man lives and doth not live,
Doth not live, not die.

In Siberia's wastes
Are sands and rocks.
Nothing blooms of green or soft,
But the snow-peaks rise aloft,
And the gaunt ice-blocks.

And the exile there
Is one with those;
They are part, and he is part!
For the sands are in his heart,
And the killing snows.

Therefore, in those wastes
None curse the Czar.
Each man's tongue is cloven by
The north blast, that heweth nigh
With sharp scimitar.

And such doom each drees,
Till hunger-gnawn,
Cold-slain, he at length sinks there;
Yet scarce more a corpse than ere
His last breath was drawn.

A.D. 1841

THE FINE OLD ENGLISH GENTLEMAN

A New Version, to be said or sung at all Conservative dinners.

by *Charles Dickens*

I'll sing you a new ballad, and I'll warrant it first-rate,
Of the days of that old gentleman who had that old estate;
When they spent the public money at a bountiful old rate
On ev'ry mistress, pimp, and scamp, at ev'ry noble gate,
    In the fine old English Tory times;
    Soon may they come again!

The good old laws were garnished well with gibbets, whips, and
   chains,
With fine old English penalties, and fine old English pains,
With rebel heads and seas of blood once hot in rebel veins:
For all these things were requisite to guard the rich old gains
    Of the fine old English Tory times;
    Soon may they come again!

This brave old code, like Argus, had a hundred watchful eyes,
And ev'ry English peasant had his good old English spies,
To tempt his starving discontent with fine old English lies,
Then call the good old Yeomandry to stop his peevish cries,
    In the fine old English Tory times;
    Soon may they come again!

The good old times for cutting throats that cried out in their
   need,
The good old times for hunting men who held their fathers'
   creed,

(223)

The gold old times when William Pitt, as all good men agreed,
Came down direct from Paradise at more than railroad speed . . .
    Oh, the fine old English Tory times;
    When will they come again!

In those rare days the press was seldom known to snarl or bark,
But sweetly sang of men in pow'r, like any tuneful lark;
Grave judges, too, to all their evil deeds were in the dark;
And not a man in twenty-score knew how to make his mark.
    Oh, the fine old English Tory times;
    Soon may they come again!

Those were the days for taxes, and for war's infernal din;
For scarcity of bread, that fine old dowagers might win;
For shutting men of letters up, through iron bars to grin,
Because they didn't think the Prince was altogether thin,
    In the fine old English Tory times;
    Soon may they come again!

But Tolerance, though slow in flight, is strong-wing'd in the
    main:
That night must come on these fine days, in course of time was
    plain;
The pure old spirit struggled, but its struggles were in vain;
A nation's grip was on it, and it died in choking pain,
    With the fine old English Tory days,
    All of the olden time.

The bright old day now dawns again; the cry runs through the
    land,
In England there shall be dear bread—in Ireland, sword and
    brand;
And poverty, and ignorance, shall swell the rich and grand,
So rally round the rulers with the gentle iron hand,
    Of the fine old English Tory days;
    Hail to the coming time!

A.D. 1842

THE LOST LEADER

by Robert Browning

Just for a handful of silver he left us,
   Just for a riband to stick in his coat—
Found the one gift of which fortune bereft us,
   Lost all the others she lets us devote;
They, with the gold to give, doled him out silver,
   So much was theirs who so little allowed:
How all our copper had gone for his service!
   Rags—were they purple, his heart had been proud!
We that had loved him so, followed him, honored him,
   Lived in his mild and magnificent eye,
Learned his great language, caught his clear accents,
   Made him our pattern to live and to die!
Shakespeare was of us, Milton was for us,
   Burns, Shelley, were with us—they watch from their graves!
He alone breaks from the van and the freemen,
   He alone sinks to the rear and the slaves!
We shall march prospering—not through his presence;
   Songs may inspirit us—not from his lyre;
Deeds will be done—while he boasts his quiescence,
   Still bidding crouch whom the rest bade aspire:
Blot out his name, then, record one lost soul more,
   One task more declined, one more footpath untrod,
One more for devils'-triumph, and sorrow for angels,
   One wrong more to man, one more insult to God!
Life's night begins: let him never come back to us!
   There would be doubt, hesitation, and pain,
Forced praise on our part—the glimmer of twilight,
   Never glad, confident morning again!

(225)

Best fight on well, for we taught him—strike gallantly,
    Menace our heart ere we master his own;
Then let him receive the new knowledge and wait us,
    Pardoned in heaven, the first by the throne!

❦

Wordsworth, who had been one of the earliest singers of freedom
and republicanism, was an inspiration to younger writers. But, as he
aged, he clung less firmly to his youthful ideals. The last straw came
in 1842 when he accepted a pension from the Crown. A young poet,
Robert Browning, penned these verses of dismay. Wordsworth was
not about to change back; the next year he accepted the official posi-
tion of poet laureate to Queen Victoria.

THE SONG OF THE SHIRT

by Thomas Hood

With fingers weary and worn,
  With eyelids heavy and red,
A woman sat, in unwomanly rags,
  Plying her needle and thread—
    Stitch! stitch! stitch!
In poverty, hunger, and dirt,
  And still with a voice of dolorous pitch
She sang the "Song of the Shirt."

"Work! work! work!
While the cock is crowing aloof!
  And work—work—work,
Till the stars shine through the roof!
It's oh! to be a slave
  Along with the barbarous Turk,
Where woman has never a soul to save,
  If this is Christian work!

"Work—work—work
Till the brain begins to swim;
  Work—work—work
Till the eyes are heavy and dim!
Seam, and gusset, and band,
  Band, and gusset, and seam,
Till over the buttons I fall asleep,
  And sew them on in a dream!

"Oh, men, with Sister dear!
  Oh, men, with Mothers and Wives!

It is not linen you're wearing out,
   But human creatures' lives!
     Stitch—stitch—stitch,
   In poverty, hunger, and dirt,
Sewing at once, with a double thread,
   A Shroud as well as a Shirt.

"But why do I talk of Death?
   That Phantom of grisly bone,
I hardly fear his terrible shape,
   It seems so like my own—
   It seems so like my own,
   Because of the fasts I keep;
O God! that bread should be so dear,
   And flesh and blood so cheap!

"Work—work—work!
   My labor never flags.
And what are its wages? A bed of straw,
   A crust of bread—and rags.
That shattered roof—and this naked floor—
   A table—a broken chair—
And a wall so blank, my shadow I thank
   For sometimes falling there!

"Work—work—work!
From weary chime to chime,
   Work—work—work,
As prisoners work for crime!
   Band, and gusset, and seam,
   Seam, and gusset, and band,
Till the heart is sick, and the brain benumbed,
   As well as the weary hand.

"Work—work—work,
In the dull December light,
   And work—work—work,
When the weather is warm and bright—
While underneath the eaves
   The brooding swallows cling
As if to show me their sunny backs
   And twit me with the spring.

"Oh! but to breathe the breath
Of the cowslip and primrose sweet—
   With the sky above my head,
And the grass beneath my feet;
For only one short hour
   To feel as I used to feel,
Before I knew the woes of want
   And the walk that costs a meal.

"Oh! but for one short hour!
   A respite however brief!
No blessed leisure for Love or Hope,
   But only time for Grief!
A little weeping would ease my heart,
   But in their briny bed
My tears must stop, for every drop
   Hinders needle and thread!"
With fingers weary and worn,
   With eyelids heavy and red,
A woman sat in unwomanly rags,
   Plying her needle and thread—
     Stitch! stitch! stitch!
   In poverty, hunger, and dirt,
And still with a voice of dolorous pitch—
Would that its tone could reach the Rich!—
She sang this "Song of the Shirt!"

Hood's verses may seem maudlin sentimentality today, but when they appeared in Punch over a hundred years ago they sounded a clarion call for reforms which, despite this and other clarion calls, took the better part of a century for their achievement.

A.D. 1848

KOSSUTH

by James Russell Lowell

A race of nobles may die out,
A royal line may leave no heir;
Wise Nature sets no guards about
Her pewter plate and wooden ware.

But they fail not, the kinglier breed
Who starry diadems attain;
To dungeon, axe, and stake succeed
Heirs of the old heroic strain.

The zeal of Nature never cools,
Nor is she thwarted of her ends;
When gapped and dulled her cheaper tools,
Then she a saint and prophet spends.

Land of the Magyars! though it be
The tyrant may relink his chain,
Already thine the victory,
As the just Future measures gain.

Thou hast succeeded, thou hast won
The deathly travail's amplest worth;
A nation's duty thou hast done,
Giving a hero to our earth.

And he, let come what will of woe,
Has saved the land he strove to save;
No Cossack hordes, on traitor's blow,
Can quench the voice shall haunt his grave.

"I Kossuth am: O Future, thou
That clear's the just and blott'st the vile,
O'er this small dust in reverence bow,
Remembering what I was erewhile.

"I was the chosen trump wherethrough
Out God sent forth awakening breath;
Came chains? Came death? The strain He blew
Sounds on, outliving chains and death."

In 1848 a wave of revolution, nationalist and sociological, swept
Europe from the Italian boot north to Germany and France. Louis
Kossuth, the Hungarian reformer, was only one of many who chal-
lenged the political strait-jacket in which the whole continent had
struggled since the end of the Napoleonic Wars.

A.D. 1850

THE SICK STOCKRIDER

by Adam Lindsay Gordon

Hold hard, Ned! lift me down once more, and lay me in the
    shade.
    Old man, you've had your work cut out to guide
Both horses and to hold me in the saddle when I sway'd,
    All through the hot, slow, sleepy, silent ride.

The dawn at "Moorabinda" was a mist-rack dull and dense,
    The sunrise was a sullen, sluggish lamp;
I was dozing in the gateway at Arbuthnot's bound'ry fence,
    I was dreaming on the Limestone cattle camp.

We crossed the creek at Carricksford, and sharply through the
    haze,
    And suddenly the sun shot flaming forth;
To southward lay "Katâwa," with the sandpeaks all ablaze,
    And the flush'd fields of Glen Lomand lay to north.

Now westward winds the bridle path that leads to Lindisfarm,
    And yonder looms the double-headed Bluff;
From the far side of the first hill, when the skies are clear and
    calm,
    You can see Sylvesters' woolshed fair enough.

Five miles we used to call it from our homestead to the place
    Where the big tree spans the roadway like an arch;
'Twas here we ran the dingo down that gave us such a chase
    Eight years ago—or was it nine?—last March.

'Twas merry in the glowing morn, among the gleaming grass,
  To wander as we've wander'd many a mile,
And blow the cool tobacco cloud and watch the white wreaths
    pass,
  Sitting loosely in the saddle all the while.

'Twas merry 'mid the blackwoods, when we spied the station
    roofs,
  To wheel the wild scrub cattle at the yard,
With a running fire of stockwhips and a fiery run of hoofs;
  O! the hardest day was never then too hard!

Aye! we had a glorious gallop after "Starlight" and his gang,
  When they bolted from Sylvester's on the flat;
How the sun-dried reed-beds crackled, how the flint-strewn ranges
    rang
  To the strokes of "Mountaineer" and "Acrobat."

Hard behind them in the timber, harder still across the heath,
  Close beside them through the tea-tree scrub we dash'd;
And the golden-tinted fern leaves, how they rustled underneath!
  And the honeysuckle osiers, how they crash'd!

We led the hunt throughout, Ned, on the chestnut and the gray,
  And the troopers were three hundred yards behind,
While we emptied our six-shooters on the bushrangers at bay,
  In the creek with stunted box-tree for a blind!

There you grappled with the leader, man to man and horse to
    horse,
  And you rolled together when the chestnut reared;
He blazed away and miss'd you in that shallow water-course—
  A narrow shave—his powder singed your beard!

(234)

In these hours when life is ebbing, how those days when life was
    young
    Come back to us; how clearly I recall
Even the yarns Jack Hall invented, and the songs Jem Roper
    sung;
    And where are now Jem Roper and Jack Hall?

Aye! nearly all our comrades of the old colonial school,
    Our ancient boon companions, Ned, are gone;
Hard livers for the most part, somewhat reckless as a rule,
    It seems that you and I are left alone.

There was Hughes, who got in trouble through that business with
    the cards,
    It matters little what became of him;
But a steer ripped up MacPherson in the Cooraminta yards,
    And Sullivan was drown'd at Sink-or-swim.

And Mostyn—poor Frank Mostyn—died at last a frightful wreck,
    In the "horrors," at the upper Wandinong,
And Carisbrooke, the rider, at the Horsefall broke his neck,
    Faith! the wonder was he saved his neck so long!

Ah! those days and nights we squander'd at the Logans in the
    glen—
    The Logans, man and wife, have long been dead.
Elsie's tallest girl seems taller than your little Elsie then;
    And Ethel is a woman grown and wed.

I've had my share of pastime, and I've done my share of toil,
    And life is short—the longest life a span;
I care not now to tarry for the corn or for the oil,
    Or the wine that maketh glad the heart of man.

(235)

For good undone and gifts misspent and resolutions vain,
　　'Tis somewhat late to trouble. This I know—
I should live the same life over, if I had to live again;
　　And the chances are I go where most men go.

The deep blue skies wax dusty, and the tall green trees grow dim,
　　The sward beneath me seems to heave and fall;
And sickly, smoky shadows through the sleepy sunlight swim,
　　And on the very sun's face weave their pall.

Let me slumber in the hollow where the wattle blossoms wave,
　　With never stone or rail to fence my bed;
Should the sturdy station children pull the bush flowers on my
　　grave,
　　I may chance to hear them romping overhead.

🌼

Australia's settlers lived a hard, but exciting life of cattle and sheep ranching with all the attendant trimmings of theft, booze, and gun-fighting.

A.D. 1852

WELLINGTON

by Benjamin Disraeli, Earl of Beaconsfield

Not only that thy puissant arm could bind
   The tyrant of a world, and, conquering Fate,
   Enfranchise Europe, do I deem thee great;
But that in all thy actions I do find
Exact propriety; no gusts of mind
   Fitful and wild, but that continuous state
   Of ordered impulse mariners await
In some benignant and enriching wind,—
   The breath ordained of Nature. Thy calm mien
Recalls old Rome as much as thy high deed;
   Duty thine only idol, and serene
When all are troubled; in the utmost need
   Prescient; thy country's servant ever seen,
Yet sovreign of thyself, whate'er may speed.

❧

Arthur Wellesley, Duke of Wellington, lived long beyond his triumph at Waterloo and functioned as a sort of Tory elder statesman. This tribute by an up-and-coming politician has all the sincerity of gold-plated brass, but Disraeli very probably meant every word of it.

A.D. 1854

THE CHARGE OF THE LIGHT BRIGADE

by Alfred, Lord Tennyson

I

Half a league, half a league,
  Half a league onward,
All in the valley of Death
  Rode the six hundred.
"Forward, the Light Brigade!
Charge for the guns!" he said.
Into the valley of Death
  Rode the six hundred.

II

"Forward, the Light Brigade!"
Was there a man dismayed?
Not though the soldier knew
  Someone had blundered.
Theirs not to make reply,
Theirs not to reason why,
Theirs but to do and die.
Into the valley of Death
  Rode the six hundred.

III

Cannon to right of them,
Cannon to left of them,
Cannon in front of them
    Volleyed and thundered;

Stormed at with shot and shell,
Boldly they rode and well,
Into the jaws of Death,
Into the mouth of hell
    Rode the six hundred.

IV

Flashed all their sabers bare,
Flashed as they turned in air,
Sabring the gunners there,
Charging an army, while
    All the world wondered.
Plunged in the battery-smoke
Right through the line they broke;
    Cossack and Russian
Reeled from the saber stroke
    Shattered and sundered.
Then they rode back, but not,
    Not the six hundred.

V

Cannon to right of them,
Cannon to left of them,
Cannon behind them
    Volleyed and thundered;
Stormed at with shot and shell,
While horse and hero fell,
They that had fought so well
Came through the jaws of Death
Back from the mouth of hell,
All that was left of them,
    Left of six hundred.

VI

When can their glory fade?
Oh, the wild charge they made!
    All the world wondered.
Honor the charge they made!
Honor the Light Brigade,
    Noble six hundred!

❧

Cynics have observed that the English manage to make more glory from their defeats than most other nations do from victory. This major military blunder from the Crimean War (England, France, and Turkey against Russia) had nothing to commend it but a reckless waste of manpower, but it will probably live, due to Tennyson's verses, far beyond more meaningful battles like Inkerman. The war ground to an inconclusive peace in 1856.

A.D. 1857

THE PIPES AT LUCKNOW

by John Greenleaf Whittier

Pipes of the misty moorlands,
  Voice of the glens and hills;
The droning of the torrents,
  The treble of the rills!
Not the braes of broom and heather,
  Nor the mountains dark with rain,
Nor maiden bower, nor border tower,
  Have heard your sweetest strain!

Dear to the Lowland reaper,
  And plaided mountaineer,—
To the cottage and the castle
  The Scottish pipes are dear;—
Sweet sounds the ancient pibroch
  O'er mountain, loch, and glade;
But the sweetest of all music
  The Pipes at Lucknow played.

Day by day the Indian tiger
  Louder yelled, and nearer crept;
Round and round the jungle-serpent
  Near and nearer circles swept.
"Pray for rescue, wives and mothers,—
  Pray to-day!" the soldier said;
"To-morrow, death's between us
  And the wrong and shame we dread."

Oh, they listened, looked, and waited,
  Till their hope became despair;

And the sobs of low bewailing
  Filled the pauses of their prayer.
Then up spake a Scottish maiden,
  With her ear unto the ground:
"Dinna ye hear it?—dinna ye hear it?
  The pipes o' Havelock sound!"

Hushed the wounded man his groaning;
  Hushed the wife her little ones;
Alone they heard the drum-roll
  And the roar of Sepoy guns.
But to sounds of home and childhood
  The Highland ear was true;—
As her mother's cradle-crooning
  The mountain pipes she knew.

Like the march of soundless music
  Through the vision of the seer,
More of feeling than of hearing,
  Of the heart than of the ear,
She knew the droning pibroch,
  She knew the Campbell's call:
"Hark! hear ye no' MacGregor's,
  The grandest o' them all!"

Oh, they listened, dumb and breathless,
  And they caught the sound at last;
Faint and far beyond the Goomtee
  Rose and fell the piper's blast!
Then a burst of wild thanksgiving
  Mingled woman's voice and man's;
"God be praised!—the march of Havelock!
  The piping of the clans!"

Louder, nearer, fierce as vengeance,
  Sharp and shrill as swords at strife,
Came the wild MacGregor's clan-call
  Stinging all the air to life.
But when the far-off dust-cloud
  To plaided legions grew,
Full tenderly and blithesomely
  The pipes of rescue blew!

Round the silver domes of Lucknow,
  Moslem mosque and Pagan shrine,
Breathed the air to Britons dearest,
  The air of Auld Lang Syne.
O'er the cruel roll of war-drums
  Rose that sweet and homelike strain;
And the tartan clove the turban,
  As the Goomtee cleaves the plain.

Dear to the corn-land reaper
  And plaided mountaineer,—
To the cottage and the castle
  The piper's song is dear.
Sweet sounds the Gaelic pibroch
  O'er mountain glen, and glade;
But the sweetest of all music
  The Pipes at Lucknow played!

❧

Revolt, partly nationalistic, partly religious, broke out against British
rule in India in 1857. British troops and Indian regiments that remained loyal to England, put the rebellion down in little more than
a year, but not before a full catalog of heroism and atrocity had been
recorded by both sides. The British colony at Lucknow were held
under close siege and it took three different relief attempts to save
them.

(243)

A.D. 1858

THE OLD CHARTIST

by George Meredith

Whate'er I be, old England is my dam!
  So there's no answer to the judges, clear.
I'm nothing of a fox, nor of a lamb;
    I don't know how to cheat, nor how to leer;
        I'm for the nation!
    That's why you see me by the wayside here,
        Returning home from transportation.

It's Summer in her bath this morn, I think.
  I'm fresh as dew, and chirpy as the birds;
And just for joy to see old England wink
    Through leaves again, I could harangue the herds;
        Isn't it something
    To speak out like a man when you've got words,
        And prove you're not a stupid dumb thing?

They shipped me off for it; I'm here again.
  Old England is my dam, whate'er I be.
Says I, I'll tramp it home, and see the grain—
    If you see well, you're king of what you see;
        Eyesight is having,
    If you're not given, I said, to gluttony.
        Such talk to ignorance sounds as raving.

You dear old brook, that from his Grace's park
  Come bounding! on you run near my old town.
My lord can't lock the water; nor the lark,
    Unless he kills him, can my lord keep down.
        Up, is the song-note!

I've tried it, too—for comfort and renown,
  I rather pitched upon the wrong note.

I'm not ashamed—not beaten's still my boast;
  Again I'll rouse the people up to strike.
But home's where different politics jar most.
  Respectability the women like.
      This form, or that form—
The Government may be a hungry pike,
    But don't you mount a Chartist platform!

Well, well! Not beaten—spite of them, I shout;
  And my estate is suffering for the cause.—
Now, what is yon brown water-rat about,
  Who washes his old poll with busy paws?
      What does he mean by't?
It's like defying natural laws,
    For him to hope he'll get clean by't.

His seat is on a mud-bank, and his trade
  Is dirt—he's quite contemptible; and yet
The fellow's all as anxious as a maid
  To show a decent dress, and dry the wet.
      Now it's his whisker,
And now his nose, and ear; he seems to get
    Each moment at the motion brisker!

To see him squat like little chaps at school,
  I could let fly a laugh with all my might.
He peers, hangs both his forepaws; bless that fool,
  He's bobbing at his frill now! what a sight!
      Licking the dish up,
As if he thought to pass from black to white,
  Like parson into lawny bishop.

(245)

The elms and yellow reed-flags in the sun
   Look on quite grave—the sunlight flecks his side;
And links of bindweed-flowers round him run,
    And shine up doubled with him in the tide.
       I'm nearly splitting,
    But nature seems like seconding his pride,
     And thinks that his behaviour's fitting.

That isle o' mud looks baking dry with gold.
   His needle-muzzle still works out and in.
It really is a wonder to behold,
    And makes me feel the bristles of my chin.
      Judged by appearance,
   I fancy of the two I'm nearer sin,
    And might as well commence a clearance.

And that's what my fine daughter said—she meant
   Pray hold your tongue and wear a Sunday face.
Her husband, the young linendraper, spent
    Much argument thereon—I'm their disgrace.
      Bother the couple!
   I feel superior to a chap whose place
    Commands him to be neat and supple.

But if I go and say to my old hen,
   I'll mend the gentry's boots, and keep discreet,
Until they grow too violent—why, then,
    A warmer welcome I might chance to meet—
      Warmer and better.
   And if she fancies her old cock is beat,
    And drops upon her knees—so let her!

She suffered for me—women, you'll observe,
   Don't suffer for a Cause, but for a man.
When I was in the dock she showed her nerve:

I saw beneath her shawl my old tea-can
　　Trembling . . . she brought it
To screw me for my work; she loathed my plan,
　　And therefore doubly kind I thought it.

I've never lost my taste of that same tea—
　　That liquor on my logic floats like oil,
When I state facts, and fellows disagree,
　　For human creatures all are in a coil;
　　　　All may want pardon.
　　I see a day when every pot will boil
　　　　Harmonious in one great tea-garden!

We wait the setting of the dandy's day,
　　Before that time!—He's furbishing his dress—
He will be ready for it!—and I say
　　That you old dandy rat among the cress—
　　　　Thanks to hard labor!—
　　If cleanliness is next to godliness,
　　　　The old fat fellow's heaven's neighbor!

You teach me a fine lesson, my old boy!
　　I've looked on my superiors far too long;
And small has been my profit and my joy.
　　You've done the right while I've denounced the wrong.
　　　　Prosper me later!
　　Like you I will despise the sniggling throng
　　　　And please myself and my Creator.

I'll bring the linendraper and his wife
　　Some day to see you, taking off my hat.
Should they ask why, I'll answer: in my life
　　I've never found so true a democrat.
　　　　Base occupation

(247)

Can't rob you of your own esteem, old rat!
I'll preach you to the British nation.

❦

The Chartist Movement (a name harking back to the rights of freemen in the Magna Carta) began in the 1830's and fought for radical
proposals (now taken for granted) like manhood suffrage, fair elec-
tions, payment of Members of Parliament. For its time it was con-
sidered an intrusion of the devil into the gentlemanly business of
English politics and many of its members were arrested, tried, and
transported off to Australia and Canada. Twenty years later, many
Chartist reforms had been or were in the process of being adopted
and an aging, forced expatriate like Meredith's narrator could come
home.

THE WIDOW AT WINDSOR

by Rudyard Kipling

'Ave you 'eard o' the Widow at Windsor
  With a hairy gold crown on 'er 'ead?
She 'as ships on the foam—she 'as millions at 'ome,
  An' she pays us poor beggars in red.
    (Ow, poor beggars in red!)
There's 'er nick on the cavalry 'orses,
  There's 'er mark on the medical stores—
An' 'er troopers you'll find with a fair wind be'ind
  That takes us to various wars.
    (Poor beggars!—barbarious wars!)
      Then 'ere's to the Widow at Windsor,
        An' 'ere's to the stores an' the guns,
      The men an' the 'orses what makes up the forces
        O' Missus Victorier's sons.
      (Poor beggars! Victorier's sons!)

Walk wide o' the Widow at Windsor,
  For 'alf of Creation she owns:
We 'ave bought 'er the same with the sword an' the flame,
  An' we've salted it down with our bones.
    (Poor beggars!—it's blue with our bones!)
Hands off o' the sons o' the widow,
  Hands off o' the goods in 'er shop,
For the Kings must come down an' the Emperors frown
  When the Widow at Windsor says "Stop!"
    (Poor beggars!—we're sent to say "Stop!")
      Then 'ere's to the Lodge o' the Widow,
        From the Pole to the Tropics it runs—

To the Lodge that we tile with the rank an' the file,
    An' open in form with the guns.
    (Poor beggars!—it's always they guns!)

We 'ave 'eard o' the Widow at Windsor,
    It's safest to leave 'er alone:
For 'er sentries we stand by the sea an' the land
    Wherever the bugles are blown.
        (Poor beggars!—an' don't we get blown!)
Take 'old o' the Wings o' the Mornin',
    And flop round the earth till you're dead;
But you won't get away from the tune that they play
    To the bloomin' old rag over'ead.
        (Poor beggars!—it's 'ot over'ead!)
            Then 'ere's to the Sons o' the Widow,
                Wherever, 'owever they roam.
            'Ere's all they desire, an' if they require
                A speedy return to their 'ome.
            (Poor beggars!—they'll never see 'ome!)

❦

According to literary folklore, these are the lines that cost Kipling
any chance of becoming Poet Laureate. The Queen was not amused
at the flippancy of a poet's comments on her long and sullen mourning withdrawal after the death of her husband and never forgave him.

A.D. 1875

From *MILTON*

by *William Blake*

And did those feet in ancient time
  Walk upon England's mountains green?
And was the holy Lamb of God
  On England's pleasant pastures seen?

And did the Countenance Divine
  Shine forth upon our clouded hills?
And was Jerusalem builded here
  Among these dark Satanic Mills?

Bring me my bow of burning gold!
  Bring me my arrows of desire!
Bring me my spear! O clouds, unfold!
  Bring me my chariot of fire!

I will not cease from mental fight,
  Nor shall my sword sleep in my hand,
Till we have built Jerusalem
  In England's green and pleasant land.

Blake wrote his tribute to Milton at the beginning of the nineteenth
century. It was not until the last quarter that its lines began to have
meaning in the context of an English labor movement.

A.D. 1880

THE WEARING OF THE GREEN

Anonymous

Oh, Paddy dear, and did you hear the news that's going round?
The shamrock is forbid by law to grow on Irish ground:
Saint Patrick's Day no more we'll keep, his color can't be seen,
For there's a cruel law agin the wearing of the Green.
I met with Napper Tandy and he took me by the hand,
And said he, How's poor old Ireland, and how does she stand?
She's the most distressful country that ever yet was seen;
They're hanging men and women for the wearing of the Green.

Then since the color we must wear is England's cruel Red,
'Twill serve us to remind us of the blood that has been shed;
You may take the shamrock from your hat and cast it on the sod,
But never fear, 'twill take root there, though underfoot 'tis trod.
When laws can stop the blades of grass from growing as they
    grow,
And when the leaves in summertime their verdure dare not show,
Then will I change the color that I wear in my caubeen;
But till that day, please God, I'll stick to wearing of the Green.

❦

*This song of Irish Independence originated sometime late in the
eighteenth century, but it seems more suitable to insert here at a
time when England, officially and with some respect, was taking
notice of the Irish Problem. Although Gladstone pushed through
some reforms, actual Irish Independence had to wait until the 1920's.*

STIR THE WALLABY STEW

Anonymous Bush Ballad

Poor Dad he got five years or more as everybody knows,
And now he lives in Maitland Jail with broad arrows on his
  clothes,
He branded all of Brown's clean-skins and never gave a tail,
So I'll relate the family's woes since Dad got put in jail.

> Chorus: So stir the wallaby stew,
>   Make soup of kangaroo tail,
>   I'll tell you things is pretty tough
>   Since Dad got put in jail.

Our sheep were dead a month ago, not rot but blooming fluke,
Our cow was boozed last Christmas Day by my big brother Luke,
And Mother has a shearer cove for ever within hail,
The family will have grown a bit since Dad got put in jail.

Our Bess got shook upon a bloke, he's gone we don't know where,
He used to act about the shed, but he ain't acted square;
I've sold the buggy on my own, the place is up for sale,
That won't be all that isn't junked when Dad comes out of jail.

They let Dad out before his time, to give us a surprise.
He came and slowly looked around, and gently blessed our eyes,
He shook hands with the shearer cove and said he thought things
  stale,
So left him here to shepherd us and battle back to jail.

(253)

The Australian Bush and the American Wild West had much in common—a rough, carefree life, hardship and hard likker, cattle rustling and a fatalistic acceptance of its consequences. The slang of this ballad works itself out without need of a special glossary. A wallaby is a small kangaroo and no gourmet delicacy. The broad arrow is the mark placed on British prison uniforms.

A.D. 1898

ZOLA

by Edwin Arlington Robinson

Because he puts the compromising chart
Of hell before your eyes, you are afraid;
Because he counts the price that you have paid
For innocence, and counts it from the start,
You loathe him. But he sees the human heart
Of God meanwhile, and in His hand was weighed
Your squeamish and emasculate crusade
Against the grim dominion of his art.

Never until we conquer the uncouth
Connivings of our shamed indifference
(We call it Christian faith) are we to scan
The racked and shrieking hideousness of Truth
To find, in hate's polluted self-defence
Throbbing, the pulse, the divine heart of man.

❧

Emile Zola, the French novelist, threw a literary bombshell into
European politics in 1898 when he published an open letter, titled
J'Accuse, denouncing the verdict of guilty against Captain Alfred
Dreyfus, a French army officer charged with selling military secrets to
Germany. The Dreyfus affair was already becoming an open scandal,
but Zola's letter blew the lid off, exposing high officials in the French
government, German cover-ups, blatant forgery and, above all, an
ugly smell of anti-Semitism (Dreyfus was Jewish). Although Zola
went to jail for his temerity, the case was reopened and after further
retrials and re-examinations, Dreyfus was cleared.

Actually, Robinson's tribute is concerned less with this aspect of
Zola than with his work as a naturalistic novelist which had made
him a target for American censorship forces. The raw life served up

(255)

in Zola's novels seems fairly tame today, but at the turn of the century, his enemies saw him as a devil incarnate, a corrupter of youth and, in full cliché, a filthy Frenchman. Robinson saw farther and heralded the full exploration of man in letters as a move toward salvation rather than degradation.

A.D. 1917

BREAK OF DAY IN THE TRENCHES

by Isaac Rosenberg

The darkness crumbles away—
It is the same old druid Time as ever.
Only a live thing leaps my hand—
A queer sardonic rat—
As I pull the parapet's poppy
To stick behind my ear.
Droll rat, they would shoot you if they knew
Your cosmopolitan sympathies
(And God knows what antipathies).
Now you have touched this English hand
You will do the same to a German—
Soon, no doubt, if it be your pleasure
To cross the sleeping green between.
It seems you inwardly grin as you pass
Strong eyes, fine limbs, haughty athletes
Less chanced than you for life,
Bonds to the whims of murder,
Sprawled in the bowels of the earth,
The torn fields of France.
What do you see in our eyes
At the shrieking iron and flame
Hurled through still heavens?
What quaver—what heart aghast?
Poppies whose roots are in man's veins
Drop, and are forever dropping;
But mine in my ear is safe,
Just a little white with the dust.

Dust and mud and rats and death, this was the trench warfare of World War I, a stubborn dedication of tradition-bound generals on both sides to theories of warfare no longer valid. Isaac Rosenberg was an English artist and poet serving as a private in France. His death in 1918 extinguished what could have been a major poet.

A.D. 1917

YPRES

by Ivor Gurney

North French air may make any flat land clear and beautiful,
But East of Yores scarred was most foul and dreadful
With stuck tanks, ruined bodies needing quick honor's burial,
But yet sunset, first morning, hallowed all, awed, made mysterious
The ugly lives of land running to eastward; the Front of us,
Worse things of conflict not yet hidden unseen underground.
(Shall we also fall stricken by one steel shard, sicken
The air with stenches, that were of Gloucestershire villages,
Be buried with haste, horror; by those who were comrades before,
Lie, clovered, rot, with no hope but to make meadows quicken
When Time has cleared this dreadful earth of infinite brute
    carnages;
And left some clean stuff; earth, beautiful—as once bodies were?)
But the place was most hideous at times, of mankind all
    unheedful;
And we forgot all battle-honors—all glories storial,
Our country's birth (our great pride) that would make stir us
Even on the brink of the grave to the risk of warfare.
Only the half-light's wonder gave us remind (made heart kind)
Of the villages and dear households we had left foolish and
    all-dutiful—

(But too rashly for such vile pain, and gray hideousness)
At Ypres—the talk of soldiers was the one delight there,
The one goodness, greatness of bearing Hell-from-high without
    fear.

❦

Third Ypres or Passchendaele expended over three months and some 400,000 British soldiers to win five miles and then settle once again into the stalemate of trench warfare. Slogans of patriotism faded as men began to see themselves as human manure.

Ivor Gurney, a composer as well as a poet, lived till 1937, but he was almost as much a war casualty as if he had died at Ypres. He suffered from recurrent shell-shock which kept him much of the time in mental homes, but his verse (some composed long after the war, for he lost sense of time and kept reliving his trench experiences) ranks with that of Rosenberg and Wilfred Owen.

c. A.D. 1935

HEADLINE HISTORY

by William Plomer

Grave Charge in Mayfair Bathroom Case;
Roman Remains for Middle West;
Golfing Bishop Calls for Prayers;
How Murdered Bride was Dressed;

Boxer Insures his Joie-de-Vivre;
Duchess Denies that Vamps are Vain;
Do Women make Good Wives?
Giant Airship over Spain;

Soprano Sings for Forty Hours;
Cocktail Bar on Mooring Mast;
"Noise, more Noise!" Poet's Last Words;
Compulsory Wireless Bill is Passed;

Alleged Last Trump Blown Yesterday;
Traffic Drowns Call to Quick and Dead;
Cup-Tie Crowd sees Heavens Ope;
"Not End of World," says Well-Known Red.

❦

The trivia of the 1930's capsulized in imaginary headlines. What is pertinently frightening is the fact that, save for a few dated or specialized words—vamps, wireless—the verses ring quite as true for the 1960's.

A.D. 1937

THE OAK OF GUERNICA

by William Wordsworth

Oak of Guernica! Tree of holier power
Than that which in Dodona did enshrine
(So faith too fondly deemed) a voice divine
Heard from the depths of its aerial bower—
How canst thou flourish at this blighting hour?
What hope, what joy can sunshine bring to thee,
Or the soft breezes from the Atlantic sea,
The dews of morn, or April's tender shower?
Stroke merciful and welcome would that be
Which should extend thy branches on the ground,
If never more within their shady round
Those lofty-minded Lawgivers shall meet,
Peasant and lord, in their appointed seat,
Guardians of Biscay's ancient liberty.

❦

The ancient oak of Guernica . . . is a most venerable natural monument. Ferdinand and Isabella, in the year 1476, after hearing Mass in the church of Santa Maria de la Antingua, repaired to this tree, under which they swore to the Biscayans to maintain their privileges. (Wordsworth's note.)

Four hundred and sixty-one years after Ferdinand and Isabella, one hundred and twenty-seven years after Wordsworth wrote his sonnet of 1810, deploring the outrages of the Pennisular War in Spain, the rebel forces of General Franco bombed Guernica out of existence.

A.D. 1937

PROUD MOTHERHOOD
(Madrid, A.D. 1937)

by F. L. Lucas

Joe's an imp of three,
  Dolores' pride.
"One day," she dreamed, "he'll be
  Known far and wide."

Kind Providence fulfills
  Dolores' guess:
Her darling's portrait thrills
  The foreign press.

Though that's no wreath of bay
  About his hair:
That's just the curious way
  Bomb-splinters tear.

❧

*Ironic sentimentality and an enviable economy of words sketch in
three short stanzas the shock as the rest of the world was forced to
accept the real significance of air war, as rehearsed for World War
II, principally by German and Italian airplanes and personnel loaned
out to rebel General Franco.*

A.D. 1940

ANNOTATIONS OF AUSCHWITZ

by Peter Porter

I

When the burnt flesh is finally at rest,
The fires in the asylum grates will come up
And wicks burn down to darkness in the madman's eyes.

II

My suit is hairy, my carpet smells of death,
My toothbrush handle grows a cuticle.
I have six million foulnesses of breath.
Am I mad? The doctor holds my testicles
While the room fills with the zyklon B I cough.

III

On Piccadilly underground I fall asleep—
I shuffle with the naked to the steel door,
Now I am only ten from the front—I wake up—
We are past Gloucester Rd, I am not a Jew,
But scratches web the ceiling of the train.

IV

Around staring buildings the pale flowers grow;
The frenetic butterfly, the bee made free by work,
Rouse and rape the pollen pads, the nectar stoops.
The rusting railway ends here. The blind end in Europe's gut.
Touch one piece of unstrung barbed wire—

Let it taste blood: let one man scream in pain,
Death's Botanical Gardens can flower again.

V

A man eating his dressing in the hospital
Is lied to by his stomach. It's a final feast to him
Of beef blood pudding and black bread.
The orderly can't bear to see this mimic face
With its prim accusing picture after death.
On the stiff square a thousand bodies
Dig up useless ground—he hates them all,
These lives ignoble as ungoverned glands.
They fatten in statistics everywhere
And with their sick, unmillable fear of death
They crowd out peace from executioners' sleep.

VI

Forty thousand bald men drowning in a stream—
The like of light on all those bobbing skulls
Has never been seen before. Such death, says the painter,
Is worthwhile—it makes a color never known.
It makes a sight that's unimagined, says the poet.
It's nothing to do with me, says the man who hates
The poet and the painter. Six million deaths can hardly
Occur at once. What do they make? Perhaps
An idiot's normalcy. I need never feel afraid
When I salt the puny snail—cruelty's grown up
And waits for time and men to bring into its hands
The snail's adagio and all the taunting life
Which has not cared about or guessed its tortured scope.

VII

London is full of chickens on electric spits,
  Cooking in windows where the public pass.
This, say the chickens, is their Auschwitz,
  And all poultry eaters are psychopaths.

❦

Auschwitz, near Cracow in Poland, was a major concentration camp, a cog in Hitler's machine for finding a "final solution" to what he called the Jewish Question. The final solution was to kill all Jews. Prisoners were shipped in by the carload, herded naked into assembly rooms where they were gassed with the efficiently lethal zyklon B. After German scavangers had gone over the bodies for valuable gold-teeth, they were bulldozed into mass graves.

A.D. 1940

THE OTHER LITTLE BOATS

by Edward Shanks

A pause came in the fighting and England held her breath,
For the battle was not ended and the ending might be death
Then out they came, the little boats, from all the Channel
shores:
Free men were those who hauled the ropes and sweated at the
oars.
From Itchenor and Shoreham, from Deal and Winchelsea,
They put out to the Channel to keep their country free.

Not of Dunkirk was this story, but of boatmen long ago,
When our Queen was Gloriana and King Philip was the foe,
And galleons rode the narrow seas, and Effingham and Drake
Were out of shot and powder, with all England still at stake.

They got the shot and powder, they charged the guns again,
The guns that guarded England from the galleons of Spain,
And the men that helped them do it, helped them still to hold
the sea,
Men from Itchenor and Shoreham, men from Deal and
Winchelsea,
Looked out happily from Heaven, and cheered to see the work
Of their grandsons' grandsons' grandsons on the beaches of
Dunkirk.

❦

*After almost a year of what bored reporters had begun to call The
Phony War, the Germans struck across Belgium and the Netherlands,
all opposition crumbling before them. The British Expeditionary
Force of a quarter of a million men was trapped on the French-*

Belgian border. By an unbelievable effort, enlisting everything from pleasure boats to rotting scows, almost the whole force was brought safely across the channel from Dunkirk to the Dover coast although millions of dollars worth of equipment had to be left behind.

A.D. 1941

BROTHER FIRE

by Louis MacNeice

When our brother Fire was having his dog's day
Jumping the London streets with millions of tin cans
Clanking at his tail, we heard some shadow say
"Give the dog a bone"—and so we gave him ours;
Night after night we watched him slaver and crunch away
The beams of human life, the tops of topless towers.

Which gluttony of his for us was Lenten fare
Who mother-naked, suckled with sparks, were chill
Though cotted in that grill of sizzling air
Striped like a convict—black, yellow and red;
Thus were we weaned to knowledge of the Will
That wills the natural world but wills us dead.

O delicate walker, babbler, dialectician Fire,
O enemy and image of ourselves,
Did we not on those mornings after the All Clear,
When you were looting shops in elemental joy
And singing as you swarmed up city block and spire,
Echo your thought in ours? "Destroy! Destroy!"

❧

German air raids on England through 1940 and 1941 destroyed one
home out of every five in London and proved, if anything, that all-
out air attacks can help to stiffen civilian resistance.

WAR POEM

by Richard West

Many people have observed with regret that the war in South
Vietnam has not yet produced a war poet who could express
the excitement and tragedy of events in the language of
modern soldiers. Unfortunately the very language does not
make things easy for poets. A war poem, such as the one
below, is bound to require footnotes.

The heavy contact now is o'er,
   The KIA are laid to rest;
The sun now re-initiates
   De-escalation in the west.

Brave Comus in his Saigon tent
   Reads through the daily BDA;
While heli-lifted Medivac
   Attends the WIA.

The Chicom hordes are held at bay;
   The NVN from Arvin flee.
While Veenaf, twenty clicks away,
   Prestrikes within the Dee Emm Zee.

The Civic Action now begins
   As friends and former foe relate;
As psy-op cadres take the field
   And start to reconsolidate.

Their highly-motivated Pats
   Rout out the infrastructural Reds

As reconstructed peasants sleep
Upon their AID-assisted beds.

Now shout hurrah, for R & R!
For 35 and 33!
Let Slope and My together cry:
Dash down yon cup of Saigon Tea!

GLOSSARY

Line 1   heavy contact = a big battle. Friendly forces have made
contact with Charlie and a fire fight followed. Charlie
from Victor Charlie and the call-sign code for VC or Viet
Cong, should not be confused with Charlies, meaning
food in US services language.

Line 2   KIA = dead. From killed in action. Although American
corpses are always referred to as KIA, the word dead can
be used of enemy corpses.

Lines 3, 4 re-initiates de-escalation = sets.

Line 5   Comus = General Westmoreland, Commander US
Forces in South Vietnam. He should strictly be called
COMUS MACVEE (Commander US Military Assis-
tance Command Vietnam).

Line 6   BDA = Bomb Damage Assessment. These reports are a
matter of great concern and controversy.

Line 7   heli-lifted = lifted by helicopter. Compare heli-chase.
Medivac = Medical evacuation.

Line 8   WIA = wounded in action.

Line 9   Chicom = Chinese Communist. Also as a noun meaning
Communist China.

Line 10   NVN = North Vietnam. Here used to mear North Vietnam troops. Arvin = The Army of South Vietnam.

Line 11   Veenaf = South Vietnamese Air Force; clicks = kilo-
meters.

Line 12   *Prestrikes* = attacks by air preliminary to a ground attack. *Dee Em Zee* = The Demilitarized Zone between North and South Vietnam. The Z's of course pronounced Zee in the American fashion. The Zone is now militarized by both sides in the war.

Line 13   *Civic action* = social work designed to win peasants to the government.

Line 14   *relate* = to make friends with.

Line 15   *psy-op* = psychological operations; *cadres* = revolutionary development cadres of political police, paid for and trained by the CIA.

Line 16   *reconsolidate* = A US AID man asks another: "Is this hamlet reconstructed?" to which the other replies: "No, Ted. I'd say it was reconsolidated."

Line 17   *highly motivated* = An American sociological jargon phrase meaning confident, brave, or inspired. The Americans admit with regret that the Vietcong are "very highly motivated." *Pats* = People's Action Teams, engaged on Rural Reconstruction.

Line 18   *infrastructural* = the Americans say that certain hamlets have a VC infrastructure. This means that they are supporters of the VC. The word infrastructure is a jargon word designed to confuse outsiders.

Line 19   *reconstructed* = converted from Communism (see *reconsolidate*).

Line 20   *AID-assisted* = paid for by the Americans.

Line 21   *R & R* = Rest and Recreation. Local leave for American troops, mostly in Hong Kong, Bangkok, and Singapore. Popularly known as I & I, for intercourse and intoxication.

Line 22   *35* = Vietnamese astrological sign of the goat, meaning sexual virility. This number is a sure subject of giggles for Vietnamese girls. *33* = the name of the excellent local beer which Americans say gives you stomach rumbles and leprosy.

Line 23   *Slope* = Vietnamese (slope head).

Line 24   *Saigon Tea* = Cold tea served at 6s a glass to bar-girls.
           It is literally cold and tea.

❧

The Vietnam War really started before the end of World War II,
when Japanese forces still held much of what was then called Indo-
China. With the Japanese driven out, war continued between native
forces under Ho Chi-Minh and the French. France was decisively
defeated at Dienbienphu in 1954, but the uneasy compromise of two
separate states, a Communist North and a U.S.-supported South,
failed to achieve any balance. Viet Cong rebels, with the support of
Ho Chi-Minh's Northern government, constantly harried the Southern government. American aid, at first held to technical advice and
economic assistance, became full-fledged military support by the middle 1960's, and a bloody seesaw has been in operation ever since. The
United States enlisted some United Nations support for its actions,
but much of the rest of the world has taken a dim view of American
involvement. The selection above (with its copious notes) represents
a liberal English view of the conflict.

Richard West's Vietnam verses succeed on several levels. They
hold up both as grimly comic verse and as socio-political comment
and are especially revealing in their unmasking of the jargon-phrases
now popularly used by most nations to conceal hard facts of death
and destruction.

It is only in his notes that, after a good beginning, Mr. West lets
the propagandist's vice of overstatement betray him. Thus, for Line
15, the inference that all cadres are tools of the American CIA is a
left-wing twin of the conservative illusion that every urban social
service worker is a Kremlin cat's-paw. Other questionable angling of
truths and half-truths, you may enjoy discovering for yourself.

(273)

INDEX OF AUTHORS

INDEX OF FIRST LINES

(277)

(278)

Poor Dad he got five years or more as everybody knows, 253